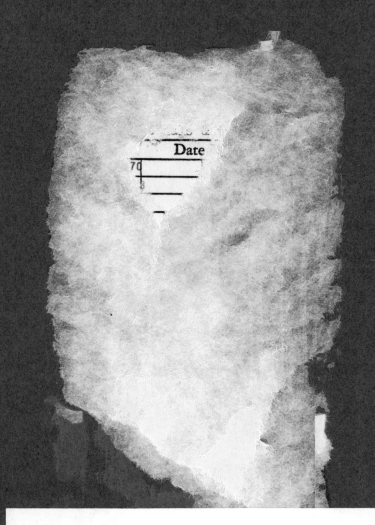

# BRIDGES, CANALS & TUNNELS

# BRIDGES, CANALS & TUNNELS

## by DAVID JACOBS and ANTHONY E. NEVILLE

Consultant

**ROBERT M. VOGEL**

*Curator, Division of Mechanical and Civil Engineering*
*Smithsonian Institution*

*Published by* **AMERICAN HERITAGE PUBLISHING CO., INC.**
*in association with* **THE SMITHSONIAN INSTITUTION**

*Book trade and institutional distribution by*
**D. VAN NOSTRAND COMPANY INC.**

# CONTENTS

# INTRODUCTION

During the first half of the nineteenth century, a succession of pioneer American trappers, traders, farmers, hunters, and herders fanned out across the Rocky Mountains to explore and exploit the riches of the West. Strictly speaking, the lands there did not belong to them: the Oregon country, with its grassy plains and dense forests, its fertile soil and abundance of wildlife, was America's and Great Britain's to share; and bountiful California, like Texas eastward and the great desert between, was the property of Mexico. Technicalities were overcome, however, by tough diplomacy and the Mexican War; and by mid-century the breadth of the continent belonged in fact to the United States.

Although they were outspokenly expansionist, the American people considered themselves neither conquerors nor colonialists. Like medieval crusaders, they believed their mission to be divinely inspired, their victories inevitable. "It is for the benefit of mankind," said Walt Whitman, that the nation's "power and territory should be extended—the farther the better." And John L. O'Sullivan, a New York newspaper editor, gave a high-sounding name to the whole expansionist mission when he wrote that America's claims to the land were justified by "our manifest destiny to overspread and to possess the whole of the continent which Providence has given us for the development of the great experiment of liberty."

The attitude embodied in the claim of Manifest Destiny reached a peak in the 1840's and remained—except during the Civil War—a major part of the American consciousness throughout the nineteenth century. Gaining impetus with the California Gold Rush of 1849, the westward movement swelled with homesteaders and ranchers, miners and merchants, and the jobless adventurers who became the cowboys. The government made it easier with liberal land grants, and trails blazed by the John C. Frémonts and Davy Crocketts were used and abused by the steady, steadily growing legions of migrants.

If the lands of the West were a lure to the American people, they also provided some formidable obstacles to the westward movement. Fast-flowing, fast-flooding rivers; huge, rocky mountains; sprawling flatlands and occasional salt lakes—all offered the resources that could make a nation unimaginably rich. Yet all stood in the way of a people westward-bound. But the obstacles had to be mastered, crossed not once but consistently, in both directions.

For the settlers, the trails were one-way routes to promised lands. For America as a whole, however, the trails would have to be expanded into a network of railroads, highways, and canals to serve not a nation of homesteads, but a nation of cities and commerce. America would become rich and powerful not simply because its crops were good, but because they could be efficiently transported and sold; not just because its mountains were rich with ores, but because the ores would be rapidly turned into alloys and the alloys into machine-made goods; not only because the ranchers bred fine, fat cattle, but because a network of inland ways would make the quick transport of whole herds or fresh meat products possible, practi-

cal, profitable. Thus, as the people went west thinking they were realizing the romance of the land, they were actually creating an urban-industrial society and the Kansas Citys, St. Louises, and Chicagos, which were the real representations of the America that was to come.

So, what the settlers in the West grew or raised went back East on technology's wheels and through technology's locks. The machinery of transport grew bigger and more powerful. Imposing locomotives pulled trainloads of goods from Wheeling on the Ohio River to Baltimore on Chesapeake Bay and back again. Paddle-wheeled steamboats hauled cargoes up and down the Mississippi. Barges transported freight back and forth between the Great Lakes and the Hudson. (Conspicuously absent was a well-coordinated network of interstate roads. Since it was commerce which was important, there was no need to develop the highways, which were too inefficient for handling freight. Families heading west in wagons had to make do with the trail blazers' roads.

Even with all the advances in transportation machinery, the natural obstacles were still present. A big, noisy locomotive would race across the land and reach the Ohio or the Delaware or the Mississippi faster than any vehicle had ever reached it before. Then it would stop and wait for a ferry and good weather. The cars or the cargo would be loaded aboard, and the vessel would cruise across the water. Waiting and the cumbersome procedure often lost the time that had been gained up to the river's edge. Far ahead, the great mountains loomed, barriers to San Francisco and Seattle.

How much more time would be lost navigating the slopes of the mountains?

Bridges and tunnels were the logical and by no means new solutions to the problems of water- and incline-barriers. But problem-solving was slow and expensive. Nothing as heavy as a train had had to cross a bridge before; nothing as important as commerce had ever compelled men to dig a hole five miles through a gigantic mountain to save a few minutes' travel time.

The problems were not unique to the United States, but the solutions had a unique effect. Abroad, transportation systems and the paths, passages, and crossings on which the systems operated were created to serve an existing society. In America, they helped to create the society. Just as the Erie Canal made a unified state out of the varied regions called New York, and just as the Baltimore and Ohio, the Pennsylvania, and the Erie railroads made a political-economic unit out of the geographically linked states comprising the East, so did the Wheeling Bridge, the Hoosac Tunnel, the Eads Bridge, and hundreds of other structures sweep away many of the great barriers between regions and make a single, unified nation. The decline of the passenger railroad and canal may have removed some of the structures from the public consciousness, and the rise of the automobile may have supplanted them with structures more impressive. But neither erased the importance of the early structures as progenitors. Even the airplane is dependent on the network of ways, as its passengers cross new bridges and new tunnels and new roads on concrete-blazed trails between city and airport.

I t did not require extraordinary vision to perceive that the United States was going to become a very large nation in a very short time, and Geneva-born Albert Gallatin had perceived as much almost as soon as he had arrived in Massachusetts from Europe in 1780. He had been nineteen years old then, and the vast lands to the west remained in his mind as he became an American, a Pennsylvanian, a politician, and a statesman. Identified with all nationalist and expansionist causes, Gallatin was appointed Secretary of the Treasury by Thomas Jefferson in 1801; he worked closely with the President to negotiate the Louisiana Purchase, to launch the government-funded Cumberland Road, and to plan the famous Lewis and Clark expedition across the North American continent to the Pacific Ocean. Steadfastly, he championed his belief in federal sponsorship of internal improvements.

In 1807, with the yawning approval of a Congress indifferent to the subject, Gallatin ordered a survey of all existing paths and passages in the young republic. He also tried to measure trends of movement and probable areas of future expansion.

Gallatin presented his report on April 4, 1808, and stated his case at the outset. "Good roads and canals," he wrote, "will shorten distances, facilitate commercial and personal intercourse, and unite . . . the most remote quarters of the United States. No other single operation, within the power of Government, can more effectually tend to strengthen and perpetuate that Union which secures external independence . . . and internal liberty."

*Weeds choke a narrow lock on a long-deserted section of the Erie Canal.*

Toward these ends, he recommended a three-part program: first, the creation of an inland waterway that would connect North and South by canals joining existing rivers from Massachusetts to North Carolina, and the construction of a highway stretching from Maine to Georgia; second, that the major rivers of the East should be developed for navigation and linked with the midwestern rivers by a series of east-west turnpikes across the Alleghenies; third, the establishment of canals that would connect the Atlantic seacoast with the Great Lakes and the St. Lawrence River. Gallatin estimated that the whole network could be built for about twenty million dollars—two million per year for a decade.

Although Gallatin's efforts won high praise, and the good sense of his report admitted, Congress never adopted his program. It was ahead of its time. A great many Americans opposed the idea of federal sponsorship of internal improvements, in part because they distrusted a strong central government, in part because they believed the Constitution did not permit it. President Jefferson, himself an advocate of such programs, believed a constitutional amendment would be required. Gallatin thought that the Constitution might, to a certain extent, be circumvented, since such a communications system would have obvious military importance. Congress was unconvinced.

It has been written that the Gallatin Report became the quasi-official statement of national policy toward inland roads and canals, but this is not precisely so. The report was prophetic, and most of its program was realized, but it

was not the federal government that did the job or that acted as a great coordinator of independent efforts. The importance of the report lies in the fact that it set forth a program for what needed to be done and inadvertently foretold what would in fact be done. But for a long time it fell to local governments, spurred by local ambitions, to accomplish what Gallatin had recommended.

One of Gallatin's suggested routes, a canal linking the Hudson River with the Great Lakes, had been proposed to New Yorkers long before the American Revolution, and the idea had reappeared consistently thereafter. In the 1790's, a corporation was actually formed in New York State to build a canal along the Mohawk. The company failed, but the idea remained alive. In 1808, Judge Joshua Forman introduced a resolution in the state legislature that called for an investigation into the feasibility of constructing a canal between the Hudson and Lake Erie. A modest six-hundred-dollar appropriation was approved, and James Geddes, a lawyer from Onondaga County, was appointed to make preliminary surveys. The enthusiastic young surveyor spent seventy-three dollars of his own money over and above the appropriation and returned with two possible routes: one using Lake Ontario part of the way, the other entirely inland.

De Witt Clinton, then the powerful, active, and flamboyant mayor of New York City, decided to become a supporter of the canal project. His original reason for supporting it was less than noble. His chief political opponent was for it, and he judged that the public would

want it; so he became a canal champion. But once he was involved with the project, Clinton became increasingly convinced of its importance to the state of New York. It is generally agreed that without his labors there might never have been an Erie Canal.

Gouverneur Morris, once a member of the Constitutional Convention, later the minister to France, was appointed chairman of the committee to plan and oversee construction of the Erie Canal. The committee proposed a waterway, following Geddes' interior route, that would run level alongside the Mohawk River from the Hudson to Utica, and then begin a gentle upward slope all the way to Lake Erie. The inclination would provide a current sufficient to propel boats eastward; westbound boats could be towed by teams of mules or horses walking the canal's embankments. Construction of the incline, however, would have been enormously expensive (across one valley it would have required an aqueduct one hundred and fifty feet high), and the committee adopted an alternate plan. This called for construction of a series of locks and aqueducts to maintain a level plane throughout—a more economical project, but one which presented a much greater challenge to engineers.

Progress on the canal surveys was slowed by the War of 1812, giving opponents of the waterway time to gather strength. They recalled previous failures to dig a canal in roughly the same place. They pointed out that the Middlesex Canal near Boston, although frequently used, had never shown a profit—and the Erie would be thirteen times as long. Downstate

*Chief wonder of the Erie Canal was Lockport's five pairs of locks (left), which carried the waterway by 12-foot lifts over the sheer Niagara escarpment. Eastbound traffic, like the boat descending at left, could pass westbound boats in the right-hand series while their tow horses used the ramp. Today, the restraining gates are gone. At right, overflow from the modern barge canal that has replaced the outmoded Erie cascades down the 66-foot drop.*

farmers disliked the idea of their taxes going to benefit farmers upstate. A few New York City businessmen, oblivious to the commercial activity the canal would generate for their own harbor, saw the canal as a boon only to cities in northern New York State.

Clinton, however, used the war years to sell his own arguments for the canal. He convinced the merchants of their shortsightedness and persuaded the farmers that tributaries of the waterway would eventually benefit their areas. By the spring of 1817, when he was a candidate for governor, the weight of public opinion was solidly in favor of the canal. And with its establishment virtually the sole issue of the campaign, Clinton was elected by an incredible margin of 43,310 to 1,479.

On Independence Day, 1817, with all appropriate ceremony, the Erie Canal was begun. It was to be by far the longest man-made waterway of its time. A spurt of canal-building had taken place in Great Britain during the second half of the eighteenth century, but together the British canals did not match the 363 miles of the Erie. Moreover, the Americans faced a forested wilderness of rough terrain that would have to be cleared before they could even start digging. The canal itself would have to cut through hills, cross swift-running streams, and cope with a 568-foot difference in water levels at its terminals (Buffalo and Albany). The project would have been a challenge to the best-trained engineers of the day; as it turned out, it was accomplished by rank amateurs.

The job of surveying and plotting the course of the canal fell to three country lawyers for whom surveying had been a profitable side line. James Geddes took charge of the western section from Lake Erie to the Seneca River; Benjamin Wright, the center section from the Seneca to Rome; and Charles C. Broadhead, the eastern section from Rome to Schoharie Creek. Without benefit of modern topographical survey procedures, they completed surveys of remarkable accuracy and thoroughness. Every mile of the route was accounted for; the terrain was fully described; the soil had been analyzed; and all the barriers, such as streams and steep hills, were clearly listed. Where Wright's surveyed section met Geddes' section, the difference in their plotted levels for the canal was less than an inch and a half.

By the autumn of 1817, rows of surveyors' stakes marking the right-of-way had been planted in both directions from Rome, where the digging would begin. The outermost rows, sixty feet apart, marked the total area to be cleared; two inner rows of stakes, forty feet apart, marked the width of the channel itself.

Shovels and axes began swinging. Wages of eighty cents a day plus meals attracted workers from throughout the state, and then Irishmen newly arrived in New York City. With teams of horses and an ingenious, gigantic contraption for pulling stumps, they cleared the right-of-way. With horse-drawn scrapers and sharp plows for cutting through thick roots, they dug the channel to a depth of four feet, sloping the embankments in such a way that though forty feet wide at top, it was only twenty-eight feet wide at bottom. Even so, the designers of the canal feared boat-generated

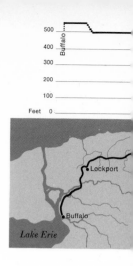
waves could undermine the embankments. To slow the traffic and dissipate such waves, they constructed sections of the canal as a series of curves. (The traffic would indeed be slow: William Cullen Bryant recalled the time a young man hopped off a canalboat, leisurely picked a basket of strawberries, and rejoined the boat after it had negotiated a curve.)

The design of the canal, especially of its locks and aqueducts, ideally called for a profound knowledge of engineering, a knowledge that was rare in the United States. The canal commission had tried to employ as supervisor a widely experienced English engineer, William Weston, who had worked on the short canal along the Mohawk in the 1790's. But even he was intimidated by the size and complexity of the task and refused the commission's generous offer. Geddes and Wright, the two most experienced lawyer-surveyors, were then put in charge as engineers. So competent did they prove to be, and so skilled their assistants, that the first generation of American engineers may be said to have sprung from the making of "Clinton's Ditch."

When construction of the Erie Canal got under way in 1817, Wright, officially in charge of the central section, served almost from the start as the unofficial chief engineer. He had a quick grasp of technical matters, was a splendid administrator, and had a particular gift for choosing able assistants. One of them was a frail young man named Canvass White, whom Wright dispatched to England to learn how canals were constructed there. He returned laden with sketches and firsthand information and

impressed especially with the British use of waterproof cement. White discovered, in the vicinity of the Erie Canal, a limestone rock that made an excellent cement, and his "waterproof lime" became the mortar that permitted stronger retaining walls and more durable and watertight locks and aqueducts.

One of the canal's most difficult technical problems was assigned to Nathan S. Roberts, another surveyor-turned-engineer. Northeast of Buffalo lay an abrupt change of terrain, a steep, rocky escarpment the canal would have to breach. With no expert available and only books to instruct him, Roberts devised a double set of five locks—one set for eastbound traffic, the other for westbound—to carry boats over a change in canal level of sixty-six feet. Around these spectacular structures, which had to be blasted from solid rock, a town was built and named, appropriately, Lockport.

All told, there were eighty-three locks on the Erie Canal, and boats were raised or lowered a total of 675 feet over the length of the waterway. The Erie engineers needed no innovations in concept to build their locks, for the system they employed was several centuries old and based on the natural phenomenon that water will always find its own level. A lock serves as a step in a canal. Basically, it is a walled enclosure with a pair of solid, hinged gates at each end. Within each gate is a small door, called a wicket, which opens on a pivot to regulate the flow of water in and out of the lock. (On the Erie, the gates sometimes contained several wickets.) Before a boat traveling downstream can enter the lock, the wicket on the

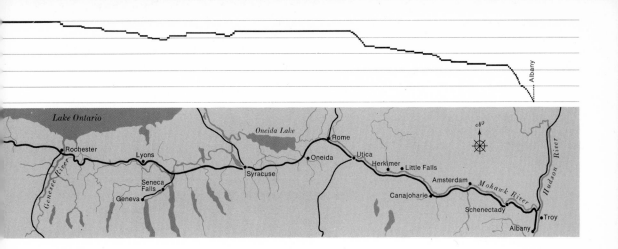

upstream (near) side is opened to allow water to flow in. When the level of water in the lock reaches that of the canal where the boat is waiting, the main gate on the upstream side is opened and the boat passes into the lock. That gate is closed, and then the wicket on the downstream (far) side is opened to allow water to pour out of the lock. When the water level in the lock is down to that of the canal on the downstream side, the lower main gate is opened and the boat passes out of the lock. For boats traveling upstream, the process is simply reversed. Most of the early locks on the Erie were fifteen feet wide and ninety feet long, and the average raising or lowering of a boat was slightly more than eight feet—which meant that more than eighty thousand gallons of water were moved in and out of a lock each time it operated.

The greater challenge to the Erie's engineers was the series of streams and rivers that lay in the path of the canal. In some instances, the engineers simply built a crude bridge to carry the towpath and a dam to hold the stream, allowing the canalboats to pass through the slack water behind the dam. But that solution was not adequate for streams with widely fluctuating currents and not very permanent for streams that were subject to violent spring floods. In most cases, streams had to be crossed without mixing waters, and so the engineers turned to an ancient technique—they carried the canal across on aqueducts.

Although aqueducts had been widely used by the Romans (to transport water for drinking and irrigation, however, not to carry boats) and were known to other civilizations, seldom were so many erected in so short a time so close together. Typically, an Erie Canal aqueduct crossed a stream on a series of parallel stone piers. These piers were linked along one side by stone arches that supported the towpath. On the other side of each pier a stone pillar was built upon the base. In profile, therefore, each pier was in the shape of a squared-off U; the canal itself, in the form of a wide, wooden trough, ran from pier to pier in the interior space of the U. The longest such aqueduct—1,188 feet—crossed the Mohawk below Schenectady on twenty-six stone piers. The aqueduct over the Genesee at Rochester was a massive structure, supporting both canal and towpath on nine Romanesque arches, each fifty feet wide. When completed in 1823, it had the distinction of being the longest stone-arch bridge in the world—802 feet. Unfortunately, it was built of a local sandstone that proved particularly weak, and the fear of imminent collapse caused the aqueduct to be abandoned and replaced ten years later.

More than three hundred smaller and simpler bridges were erected across the canal itself. Governor De Witt Clinton had promised not to interfere with the farmers' ability to develop their property, and he kept his promise by erecting a series of "occupation bridges," some only seven feet above water. These simple bridges—often made from planks of timber laid across the width of the canal—reconciled the farmers whose land was cut by the Erie, although they caused not a few headaches for canalboat passengers who forgot to duck.

Meanwhile, the canal itself became a temporary but serious headache for Clinton. The construction costs were mounting, and work was being slowed by bad weather, outbreaks of malaria, and the rough terrain that had been deliberately avoided in the early stages of construction. By 1822, opposition to Clinton and his project had grown so strong that his few remaining backers dared not nominate him for a second term as governor. Later that year, several sections of the canal were opened and boats began to run from Little Falls to Schenectady. But Clinton's stock continued to fall, and early in 1824 his political enemies, now firmly in power, removed him from the canal commission altogether. It was their last, desperate attempt to ruin him. Early in the fall financial reports were issued, showing that the Erie Canal, even though unfinished, was already earning money, and the back of the opposition was broken. Clinton was elected governor again, and stood by his promise that the canal would be finished in the fall of 1825.

On October 26 of that year, Governor Clinton boarded a boat called the *Seneca Chief* at Buffalo to play preacher in a "Wedding of the Waters." A cannon boomed and Clinton's vessel, carrying two kegs of water from Lake Erie, began the journey eastward. Other boats fell in behind, forming a procession that was welcomed by grand festivities on farm after farm, in town after town, all the way to the Hudson. On November 2, the fleet reached New York Harbor; at nearby Sandy Hook, Clinton poured the Erie water into the Atlantic and consummated the marriage.

The Erie Canal was an instant and enormous success. Not only did it operate profitably, but it reduced shipping costs tenfold (from one hundred dollars per ton to ten dollars), increased land values in upstate New York, and stimulated settlement in the Great Lakes region. In 1826, when as many as fifty boats a day were starting westward from Albany, tolls on the Erie and the adjoining Champlain Canal amounted to $765,000. Once deprecatingly called Clinton's Ditch, in the days when it seemed impossible to build, the Erie was now referred to as the Grand Canal.

The people of other states looked upon New York's canal with new respect and with justified fear of losing business to it. Out of interstate rivalry, it now appeared, much of Albert Gallatin's program for internal improvements would come to fruition. Even before the Erie was finished, new canals—and extensions of canals long abandoned—were being built in Pennsylvania, New Jersey, and several of the New England states. By 1830, boats were plying more than eight hundred miles of waterway in New York, Pennsylvania, Delaware, and Maryland; another thirteen hundred miles were under construction.

The canal craze was on. In most instances, the ambitious projects were undertaken by state governments; the private entrepreneurs stuck to the short courses—and usually made better profits. The Michigan legislature recklessly committed itself to raising fifty million dollars in bonds for a system of canals and railroads at a time when it was still a wilderness with a population slightly over one hundred

The gangs of laborers (mostly Irishmen), who cleared a 60-foot-wide swath through the wilderness for the Erie Canal, were the forerunners of some 1.5 million immigrants (left) who landed in New York between 1820 and 1850. Along with farm families tired of scratching a living from rock-bound New England, these Europeans crammed the westbound canalboats, heading for the fertile farmlands and rich pine stands of the Ohio country. The fruits of their labors there increased the Erie's eastbound tonnage tenfold in a single decade, adding more than two million dollars to the canal's earnings. Hundred-passenger packet boats plied night and day, whipping up their horses to break the speed limit (four miles an hour) and forcing slower craft to drop towlines and move aside. Nowadays, trees separate an abandoned stretch of canal from the towpath that was once so integral to its existence.

*In the heyday of the canal era, thousands of families lived out their lives on the slow freight boats that plied the inland waterways. In 1845 some 25,000 men, women, and children were working 4,000 boats on the Erie Canal alone. By the 1880's, however, boat travel on Pennsylvania's Lehigh Canal—one of the many waterways superseded by the railroads—had become a nostalgic holiday pastime for wealthy Philadelphians (below).*

thousand people. Many of the states lost enormous sums from their projects, though they gained incalculably from the waves of settlers borne westward over the canals, and the commercial development that followed so quickly upon their arrival.

De Witt Clinton lent his awesome presence to the ceremonies launching several of these canals, and his self-trained engineers went forth to supervise the building of many of them. Canvass White became chief engineer for the Union Canal of Pennsylvania and later acted as chief engineer of the Delaware and Raritan in New Jersey and the Lehigh Canal in Pennsylvania simultaneously. His frail health gave under the strain; he retired to Florida before the projects were finished and died at the age of forty-four. Nathan Roberts lent his talents to the Chesapeake and Delaware, the Pennsylvania State Canal, and the Chesapeake and Ohio before being called back to the Erie in 1839 to supervise part of its widening to accommodate constantly increasing traffic. Benjamin Wright, mentor of both White and Roberts, became consulting engineer for a number of canals, then changed his allegiance to railroads. John B. Jervis, who began as an axman on the Erie, succeeded Wright as supervisor of the Delaware and Hudson Canal; like Roberts, he later worked on widening a section of the Erie.

No more formidable challenge faced the Erie alumni than the route proposed from Philadelphia to Pittsburgh. Pennsylvania needed a fast, efficient route to the West; the Erie Canal was stealing the state's commerce, and Philadelphia, which aspired to be the largest American city, was fast losing that distinction to New York. Freight from Philadelphia to Columbus, Ohio, took thirty days to get there, at a cost of a nickel a pound. Shipping it from New York City through the Erie Canal took only twenty days, at half the price. Although Pennsylvania had a few canals, some begun in the 1790's and later abandoned, it also had the Allegheny Mountains. A canal to Pittsburgh would require five times as much lockage as the Erie. The solution, designed by Canvass White, was a portage railroad over the mountains.

A canal was dug eastward from Pittsburgh to Johnstown, where the portage railroad took over for the crossing of the Alleghenies. On the other side of the mountains, another canal paralleled the Juniata and Susquehanna rivers as far as Columbia, Pennsylvania. There another problem arose. The Union Canal, recently completed at a cost of six million dollars to link the Susquehanna with Philadelphia, was judged too narrow for commercial usefulness; its locks were only eight and a half feet wide, and none of its boats could carry more than twenty-eight tons of cargo. And so the state legislature authorized the building of a railroad to cover the eighty-one miles. It was the first railroad to be sponsored by a government and a harbinger of a new era that would supersede the great period of canal-building.

By the mid-1830's the new route from Philadelphia to Pittsburgh was completed. It was, of course, a complicated passage, requiring changes in mode of transportation at a number of points, but the four-hundred-mile trip could now be made in five days. The route became a major artery to the West and it attracted a fair number of excursionists, especially to the dizzying delights of Canvass White's portage railroad over Allegheny Mountain. Charles Dickens, who enjoyed the trip in 1842, described the railroad in his *American Notes:* "There are ten inclined planes; five ascending, and five descending; the carriages are dragged up the former, and let slowly down the latter, by means of stationary engines; the comparatively level spaces between, being traversed, sometimes by horse, and sometimes by engine power, as the case demands." Each of the inclined planes had two sets of tracks, and for every ascending car there was a descending one, connected to the first by cable looped around the drum of the stationary engine, to act as counterweight.

But the Pennsylvania route was a dismal financial failure. The tolls did not even pay the interest on the debt the state had incurred in building it. For one thing, the route was complicated, cumbersome, and slow; there were more locks along the eastern portion of the canal than on the entire Erie, which was more than three times as long. The portage railroad was expensive to operate. It was also a bottleneck to traffic, which took three hours just to get up one side of the mountain. To the chagrin of the politicians, Philadelphia merchants still preferred to ship by the Erie Canal.

The state of Pennsylvania clung to its dubious assets, hoping against hope that prosperity for the canals was just around the corner. Costs rose and revenues fell. In the meantime, private interests leased the state-owned track between Philadelphia and Columbia and began building a railroad from the Susquehanna to Pittsburgh, often parallel to the canal route. The enterprise prospered, and in 1857 the state finally gave up and sold its entire Philadelphia-Pittsburgh route to this newly incorporated rival: the Pennsylvania Railroad.

The same struggle between canal and railroad had already been acted out not far to the south, and with the same result. On Independence Day, 1828, the merchants of Baltimore launched an enterprise that would bring prosperity to their port city: the Baltimore and Ohio Railroad. Charles Carroll, ninety-one years old and the only surviving signer of the Declaration of Independence, dug the first spadeful of earth for the placing of the commemorative stone. On that same day, in Georgetown, barely forty miles away, John Quincy Adams was digging the first spadeful of earth for the Chesapeake and Ohio Canal. It took the President three tries to get the spade into the earth, and to those who looked for such things, this might have been taken as a striking omen. Progress on the Chesapeake and Ohio was slowed and periodically halted by miserable terrain, lawsuits, lack of new capital, epidemics, and feuds among the laborers, who came from rival counties of Ireland. Not until 1850 did the canal reach 185 miles to Cumberland, Maryland, at a cost per mile of about sixty thousand dollars, three times that of the Erie. There it stopped, far short of the Ohio River.

Twilight had fallen on the canal era. The bright day for the railroads had begun.

# TIMBER SPANS
# AND IRON HORSES

A commonly neglected aspect of the subject of the railroad is the fact that it is before all else a road of rails. To some extent this neglect is understandable. It is, after all, the train rather than the track that occupies so much space in American history and lore. Almost everyone has memories of the trains that passed by him in his childhood, and there are legions of railroad buffs and scores of railroad scholars who feed the nostalgia. But their memories and studies dwell on the great steam- and later diesel-powered locomotives, their respective differences and advantages, and the romantic missions they accomplished. As for the rails—the rails are there because the trains run on them; the rails are what one uses to explain perspective to a child.

It can come as a jolt, then, to be reminded that the rails were not tailor-made to suit the needs of the locomotive, and that in fact the locomotive was developed to make use of rails that were already roads. When the nation's first major railroad, the Baltimore and Ohio, was chartered in 1827, the steam locomotive was a brand-new invention of doubtful practicality. The B & O's original locomotive was a horse of flesh and blood, not iron.

The value of rails as roads was becoming apparent in the 1820's, even before the steam locomotive was showing promise. The faults of dirt and stone roads were demonstrated by the instant success of the completed sections of the Erie and other canal routes. On the whole, water-going vessels were slower than land vehicles, but they could carry far more freight —along routes that ran directly from port to port. Wagons, on the other hand, had to suffer overused roads that varied in condition from day to day, depending on weather, the nature of the traffic, and the amount of axle grease sopped into the earth. A railway, however—even if it were made of wood—would eliminate most of the land problems. The rail surface would provide a consistently hard and relatively level surface for rolling wheels; by reducing the burden borne by the horse, it could quicken his pace; and it would permit trains of wagons to be hauled by single teams of horses.

Men soon began to perceive that the railroad would also have advantages over the canal. In the northern states, railroads could operate during the months when canals were frozen over. And railroads would be easier and cheaper to build, requiring little more construction work than a canal's towpath requires. (It had to be acknowledged that the railroad vehicles would be costly; moreover, unlike the canalboats, they would belong to the railroad company, not to the individual merchants and farmers, and would be subject to far more regimentation in their use.)

By the mid-1820's, the logic of the railroad was impressing American legislators and investors, as was the observable success of the railroad in England. Iron rails had been introduced in England as early as 1767, and by 1825 George Stephenson had demonstrated a workable steam locomotive. Not long thereafter, railroad companies throughout the eastern United States were applying for charters. Construction of the Baltimore and Ohio began in 1828, and the founders of that railroad, well aware of the pioneering aspect of their enterprise, financed the project generously and welcomed any idea that would work. Horses pulled the cars during the first years of the railroad's operation, but other solutions were given a try, including a treadmill locomotive powered by horses and a wind-propelled sailcar. The company offered a four-thousand-dollar prize for "the best steam locomotive," but attracted only five competitors. The winner, Phineas Davis, was given not only his prize but a job, workshop, and a reasonably free hand and pocketbook with which to experiment. (Davis operated the B & O shop until 1835, when a locomotive of his own design derailed and crushed him to death.)

In addition to its distinction as the oldest surviving railroad company in the United States, the Baltimore and Ohio was destined to earn another proud title: "the first American railroad engineering school." The man in charge of the B & O's engineering department was an imaginative Pennsylvania Quaker named Jonathan Knight. Despite a fiery temper and an inclination to get involved in bitter political disputes, Knight was an ideal choice to get the railroad under way. A disciplined and brilliant surveyor and mathematician, he brought his knowledge and scientific curiosity to the new and underexplored problems that the railroad would introduce. Knight had faced the obstacles of rugged wilderness as a surveyor for the Chesapeake and Ohio Canal and the federal government's Cumberland Road, but in laying out the B & O he faced the additional

*Through colonial times, and in the early days of the republic, bridge technology was home-grown by local carpenters and surveyors. The scene below, a detail from a painting by a 20th-century carpenter, Joseph Pickett, shows two bridges of 1776, at Coryel's Ferry in Pennsylvania, close to where Washington crossed the Delaware. In the upper right-hand corner, holding a spyglass, stands history's best-known surveyor, General George Washington.*

25

*The railroad, which would revolutionize bridge-building, began as a road of rails for horse-drawn vehicles, and it was some time before the iron horse came into its own. ( At right is the celebrated race of 1830 when a horse-drawn tram, behind at first, beat the* Tom Thumb.*) But by 1850 steam locomotives were riding more than 9,000 miles of track and bridge builders had a crucial, new problem: how to contend with massive, moving weight.*

obstacle of ignorance. What was the minimum curve, or the maximum grade, that the locomotive would be able to negotiate? With no precedents to guide him, Knight proceeded by intuition to build a route that was ready for steam locomotives when they arrived. He also undertook a number of scientific studies, among them an investigation of the factors offering resistance to moving railroad cars.

There were other engineering problems to which railroads gave rise, including the need to build adequate bridges. The challenge was not simply to build bridges that would carry tremendous weight—London Bridge and the Ponte Vecchio in Florence, for example, had long borne heavy shops and other buildings—but structures that could bear concentrated, sudden weight *in motion*, that could withstand the special strains and vibrations heavy trains would create. And for American engineers the added challenge, frequently imposed on them by the railroads' managers, was to build such bridges as simply and cheaply as possible. (This zeal for economy and frequent indifference to safety was to lead to a national scandal in the 1870's.) There was no need for a radical departure from existing bridge forms, but the basic forms had to be altered and perfected to meet the new needs.

With only a few exceptions—and most of those very modern—all building techniques spring from a very few basic structural principles. Usually simple in concept and geometry, these systems apply to architecture and bridge-building alike. What in the former is called post-and-lintel construction (consisting of vertical supports and horizontal beams) is called beam- or girder-construction in the latter. Architecture's vaulting is bridge-building's arched span. Building outward from a single support is known as cantilever construction in both disciplines.

The simplest sort of bridge, of course, consists of nothing more than a plank over the water (or whatever else is to be crossed). There are obvious limitations to such a structure. It cannot be very long, else it will break; short of the breaking point, the bridge will bow downward, especially when weight is at the center, subjecting the plank to opposing stresses (compression on top, tension on the bottom). A foot passenger can expect a bouncy trip across such a structure.

There are a number of ways to overcome the faults of the basic bridge. Every few feet a pier can be added (the solid supports at the end of a bridge are called abutments; those in between are called piers) or the whole structure can be undergirded with elaborate scaffolding. The latter was the frequent choice of the builders of wooden railroad trestles in the West, and it is still preferred by "Western" movie-makers who want to depict a spectacular collapse. Or the principle of the arch can be employed, in a variety of ways. The roadway itself can be arched upward; since an arched form has a tendency to straighten itself out under pressure, part of the weight on the bridge will be distributed as a horizontal force against the abutments. Alternatively, the arch can be placed under the bridge, stretching from abutment to abutment, to give support to the roadway. The arch can

also be placed above the bridge and the roadway hung from it.

Or, a pair of ladderlike framed structures can be run from abutment to abutment (or from pier to pier) with the roadway beams laid crosswise between them, on either the top or bottom horizontal member. Adding diagonal members to the framed structure makes it a truss and greatly strengthens it: a rectangle bisected by a diagonal becomes two triangles, and the triangle is the only geometric figure that is rigid. (Though a triangle built of three rigid pieces pinned together is theoretically indestructible, in reality the strength of materials and joints must be considered. Pressure applied to any point of the triangular structure will produce tension in one or more members and compression in the others, and this is a basic concern of bridge engineering.) If the roadway is laid on the top horizontal member—which is called a chord—the bridge is a deck truss; if laid on the bottom member, it is a through truss.

Truss bridges appeared here and there in colonial America, but the technique of building them—fortunately for the railroad—advanced most rapidly in the last decade of the eighteenth century and the first decades of the nineteenth. The initial great advances were made not by trained engineers, but by master carpenters who happened to build bridges.

Timothy Palmer, self-named "the ingenious," was a carpenter in Newburyport, Massachusetts, willing to travel wherever work was to be had in the United States. His specialty was a bridge design that combined the principles of the arch and the truss, and his most famous accomplishment was the so-called Permanent Bridge over the Schuylkill River at Philadelphia, built in 1806. In profile, it consisted of three trusses mounted on the abutments and two piers set in the river bed. The bottom chord of each truss was a timber arch; the arch was structurally more important than the truss above it, and the form was technically a "trussed arch." The roadway itself was a single arch stretching thirteen hundred feet from shore to shore, resting on the three smaller arches. With uncharacteristic modesty, Palmer predicted a life span of only thirty or forty years for the bridge. Fifty-five years later the bridge was still in serviceable shape when it was destroyed by fire, like so many of the early timber bridges. The other enemy of the timber spans was weather; Palmer therefore covered his, top and sides, as did many of the other early builders. Once adopted, the covered bridge proved to have other advantages. It kept snow off the roadway, allayed the fears of livestock about crossing over streams, and proved a romantic attraction to young lovers.

Six years after it was built, the Permanent Bridge had a nearby rival as an engineering spectacle. Lewis Wernwag, a German-born Philadelphian, built a timber bridge over the Schuylkill that was then the longest in the country, a single, trussed arch 340 feet long. Aptly called the Colossus, the bridge was supported by five parallel arches stretching from shore to shore, each three and a half feet thick, constructed of laminated timbers. So strong were these supports that the trusswork above

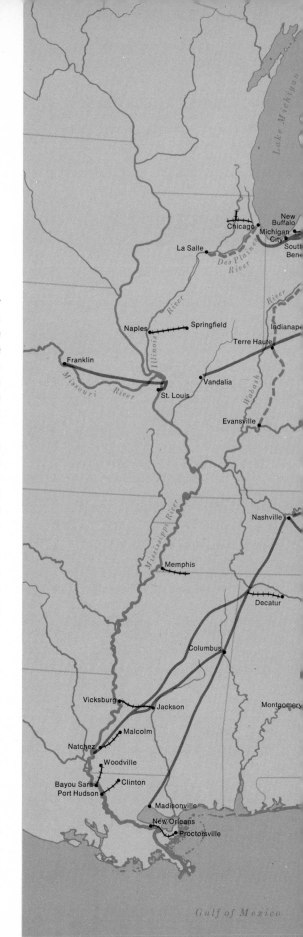

them had no weight-bearing function under normal loads. The Colossus went down in flames in 1838, and America lost what some critics still regard as the most beautiful bridge in its history. Wernwag was the first to use iron diagonals in a truss panel (in his bridge across the Delaware at New Hope, Pennsylvania) and the first to build a timber railroad bridge (for the Baltimore and Ohio).

A man who brought bridge design closer to the needs of the railroad was Theodore Burr, a relative of the more famous Aaron Burr and a New England-born carpenter who spent most of his life in Harrisburg, Pennsylvania. His basic structure was a flat truss; its top and bottom chords were straight and parallel, and either could support a level railroad track. Burr evidently lacked confidence in the self-sufficiency of the truss, however, for he superimposed the arch onto the truss as supporting member. The design inspired confidence in other bridge builders too, and it was widely used throughout the nineteenth century.

But the Burr design was not altogether satisfactory for railroad use. Under the weight of trains rumbling across it, the arch-and-truss structure created special problems. The truss put vertical pressure on the abutments, which was all right, but the arch added horizontal pressures as well. For all its massiveness, the combined form was not very efficient; the pinning together of two disparate bridge forms did not in every instance result in one bridge member bolstering the work of another. And there were too many joints in the structure, all of them subject to wear. What was needed was

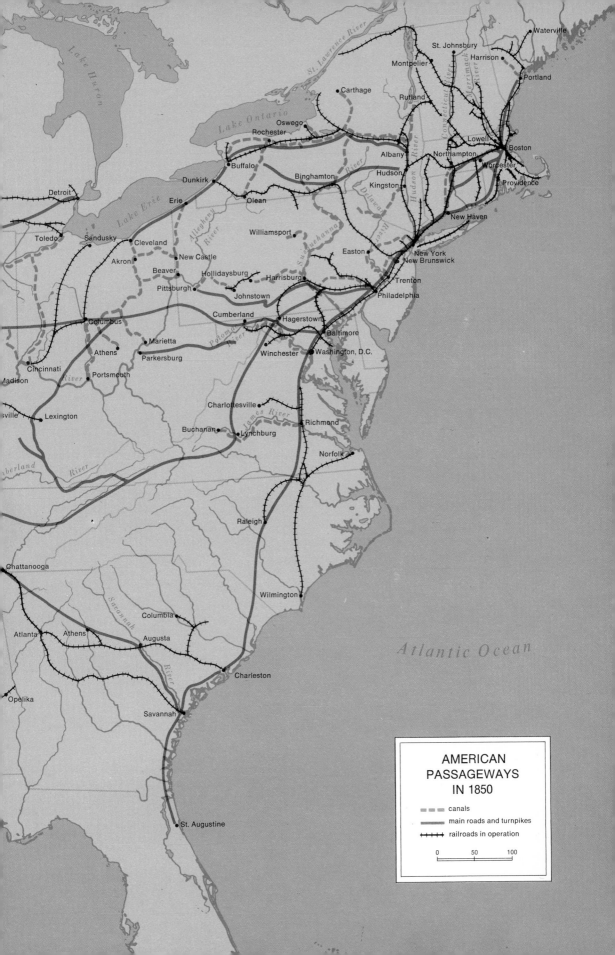

**AMERICAN PASSAGEWAYS IN 1850**

- - - canals
— main roads and turnpikes
++++ railroads in operation

0        50        100

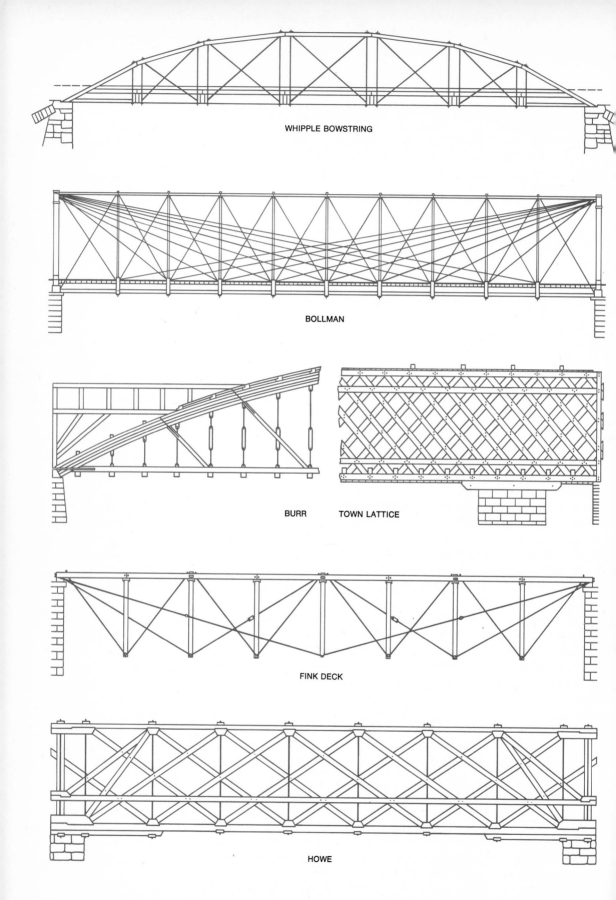

WHIPPLE BOWSTRING

BOLLMAN

BURR    TOWN LATTICE

FINK DECK

HOWE

a structure that was simpler and lighter: a truss that was just a truss.

In 1820, Ithiel Town, an architect from New Haven, Connecticut, patented a truss that was destined to serve the needs of many of the railroads in their earliest years. Town filled the space between the top and bottom chords of the truss with a latticework of diagonal pieces. The result was not only sturdy, but easy and cheap to produce, and Town boasted that his bridge could be "built by the mile and cut off by the yard." He charged a dollar a foot for every bridge built by license under his patent, and two dollars a foot whenever he found one built without his permission. The bridge design was popular, but the increasing weight of locomotives eventually proved it inadequate for railroads; in 1840 a Town truss over Catskill Creek in New York State collapsed, killed a workman, and gained the distinction of causing the first railroad-bridge fatality in the country.

The year 1840 brought an important advance for railroad-bridge engineering when William Howe, uncle of the Elias Howe who invented the sewing machine, received a patent for his truss design. His was much simpler in appearance than Town's design, requiring far fewer diagonals. More important, Howe's truss introduced wrought iron into bridge design exactly where it was needed. Wood had proved a suitable material for the bridge members under compression, but it was a poor material for members under tension, especially at the joints. Howe used wrought-iron rods as vertical tension members, running them all the way through the top and bottom chords and attaching nuts to their threaded ends so that the bridge could be tightened from time to time. This last was an ingenious touch, but occasionally subject to a reversal of its purpose: vibrations from trains tended to loosen the nuts, as did diabolical pranksters.

During the 1840's, cast iron gradually joined timber as a basic material for railroad bridges, and the Howe truss survived the conversion. Cast iron, however, proved to have limited strength under tension, and wrought iron, more expensive but more elastic, came into wider use. Eventually wrought iron was employed for entire structures and cast iron fell into disuse. The Howe truss underwent considerable modifications: the Pratt truss of 1844 resembled the Howe truss in appearance, but it reversed the functions—vertical posts became compression members and the diagonals, tension members.

The evolution of the iron truss bridge was guided by railroad men, among them the second chief engineer of the Baltimore and Ohio, Benjamin Henry Latrobe II. Son of the architect of the same name who was responsible for the neo-Greek tone of Washington, D.C., Latrobe joined the B & O as Knight's assistant in 1831 and took over when the first engineer retired in 1842. Although his work with iron bridges was to ensure his greatest fame, Latrobe's first major B & O bridge-building chore resulted not in a truss at all, but in a remarkable stone-arch viaduct at Relay, Maryland, nine miles southwest of Baltimore. The bridge, the Thomas Viaduct, was a formidable structure which cost so much and took so long to

build that it was called "Latrobe's Folly." In the best tradition of such follies, the viaduct is still standing, bearing the weight of modern railroad traffic.

In the winter of 1834, tracks of the B & O, lying along the north shore of the Potomac River, reached Harpers Ferry and a major obstacle: the precipitous Catoctin Mountain extending down to the river. A bridge would have to be built across the Potomac and the C & O Canal to the town of Harpers Ferry itself, so that the railroad could continue its westward course. It was a foregone conclusion that Lewis Wernwag would build it; he had already built one bridge for the B & O and, ten years before, had moved his lumber business to Harpers Ferry. We cannot be certain what kind of truss, or combination of arch and truss, was employed in the Wernwag bridge; in the manner of the day, Wernwag covered it, top and sides, and that is how contemporary lithographs depict it. The bridge was already completed and in use when Benjamin Latrobe found defective masonry in the piers, which had to be replaced, and a minor fracture in the wooden structure.

Among the workmen who helped with these repairs in 1838 was a young free-lance carpenter named Wendel Bollman, who had come to Harpers Ferry to build a house. In 1828, as a boy of fourteen, Bollman had marched in the Baltimore parade celebrating the beginning of the B & O, and the following year worked for the railroad, laying wooden track. At Harpers Ferry he obviously made a great impression on Benjamin Latrobe, who not only put him back on the B & O payroll but shortly thereafter

made him foreman of bridges. In 1851, when he was in charge of the B & O's right-of-way and its structures, Bollman returned to Harpers Ferry to erect an iron truss bridge of his own design. It replaced only a portion of the wooden Wernwag bridge, but it was an impressive structure nonetheless. In its official test, three locomotives rolled across the 124-foot span, distributing a weight of more than a ton per foot of bridge, yet causing a deflection at the bridge's center of less than an inch and a half. Because of its strategic importance to both armies during the Civil War, the B & O bridge suffered damage on more than one occasion, but Bollman kept repairing it and by 1870 had the entire bridge rebuilt with his own trusses.

The distinctive feature of Bollman's truss was its wrought-iron diagonal rods, which extended radially outward from the top of the end posts to each point along the bottom chord where a floor beam required support. In fact the bottom chord was structurally superfluous to the truss, and in 1851 Albert Fink, another of Latrobe's assistants, patented a design for a truss that was similar to Bollman's plan but eliminated the bottom chord when used as a deck truss. While Bollman was building his first Harpers Ferry bridge in 1851, Fink was building a more impressive structure for the B & O across the Monongahela River at Fairmont, Virginia (later West Virginia). The bridge consisted of three through trusses, each 215 feet long, in which the bottom chord was retained as a support for the roadway. Fink's crowning achievement came sixteen years later, when, for the Pennsylvania Railroad, he

built a mile-long bridge across the Ohio at Louisville, consisting of twenty-seven truss spans, most of them according to his original design.

Bollman and Fink were transitional figures in the evolution of bridge-engineering. Unlike the intuitive carpenter-designers of an earlier era, they understood something of the theory and mathematics of bridge-building. (Fink had studied in a German polytechnical school; Bollman was wholly self-taught in the subject.) But they put their trust only in the empirical approach. Frequently they built models of bridges out of scraps of metal in the B & O's repair shop and then tested them to the point of destruction. Their trusses passed the empirical test but not the theoretical. They had too many members, and hence too much dead weight, for the loads they were asked to carry.

As trains grew heavier and the iron bridges less and less adequate to support them, as the railroads approached the formidably wide rivers to the west of the Appalachians, it became increasingly clear that bridge-building required a firmer grounding in science. Design would have to follow from a precise understanding of the forces of tension and compression, the choice of materials from a careful analysis of their strengths and weaknesses.

Among the first to recognize the need was Squire Whipple, a trained surveyor who had grown up on a New York farm while the Erie Canal was being built nearby. In 1847 he published *A Work on Bridge Building*, the first American attempt to analyze bridge design mathematically and to determine the tensile and compressive strengths of various materials

for bridges. Whipple's book launched the science of bridge engineering, and in later years he issued expanded editions, making the woodcuts himself and printing the book in his home.

Whipple also contributed bridge designs of his own invention. His first, a modification of a French design, was a bowstring truss, which combined the principles of arch and truss, not as complementary structures, but integrally. The arch formed the top chord of the bridge; it was not actually round but formed of straight pieces, like the perimeter of a polygon. In 1846 Whipple patented a second design, in which the top chord was parallel to the bottom, but with the distinctive—and distinguishing—feature of end posts that were not upright but inclined inward toward the center of the bridge. Whipple's truss designs were being used well into the twentieth century, while the Bollman and Fink designs fell to disuse in the 1870's.

Like all modern engineers, Whipple built his bridges with a margin of safety, designing them to withstand weights many times those that could be expected when first put into use. "The providing of abundant strength seems the more proper," he wrote in 1869, "as the tendency has been and still is, to increase the weight of engines and loads to the utmost capacity of the track." How much that weight was to increase, how far it would outstrip the margins of safety he then employed, Whipple could hardly have imagined. In 1869, the average locomotive weighed 20 tons. By the end of the century, 150-ton locomotives would be common. The iron bridge would have to go, victim of the iron horse.

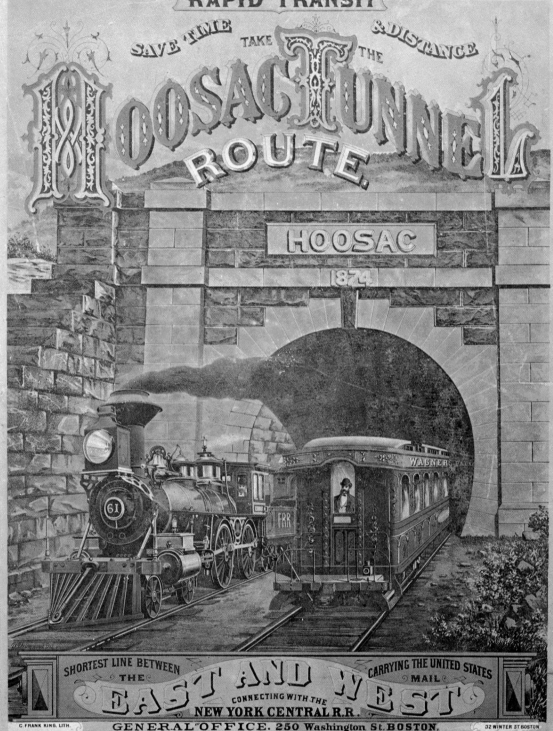

# THE IMPORTANCE
# OF BEING LEVEL

If the railroads were the necessity that mothered engineering inventiveness, they nonetheless had an important ally: the American terrain. Between the eastern coastal cities and the new western settlements lay the Appalachian Mountains and the many streams that flowed down through their valleys. For the sake of commerce and communications, the barriers had to be crossed. Railroad engineers, once they finally abandoned the idea of the inclined plane, had to master the terrain by very gradual changes in elevation. They needed bridges and, eventually, tunnels.

A few of the railroads were able to take advantage of the river valleys that extended far back into the Appalachians. The Baltimore and Ohio hugged the banks of the Potomac for much of the way to Cumberland, deep in the Appalachian range. Others were not so fortunate. The New York and Erie Railroad, born in controversy and raised in poverty and mismanagement, had no natural waterway to follow for the greater part of its course westward from the Hudson just above New York City to Dunkirk on Lake Erie. Here and there were banks of streams, but formidable mountains blocked the route from one valley to the next. To make matters worse, the New York legislature granted the company a charter only on the conditions that the railroad stay far away from the route of the Erie Canal and that it stay wholly within the state of New York. The latter condition was finally waived when the railroad reached the Delaware valley at Port Jervis and again when it reached the Susquehanna farther west.

*An 1880's poster proclaims the main attraction on the Fitchburg Railroad.*

*When it was finished in 1851, the Erie Railroad route was hailed as "the work of the age." It had crossed more rugged terrain than any other railroad in the East, and not the least of its spectacular achievements was the Starrucca Viaduct, a stone-arch bridge 1,200 feet long. A crew of 800 men built it in 1848 for the sum of $320,000, making it then the most expensive railroad bridge in the world—and also one of the most beautiful.*

Benjamin Wright surveyed the Erie route in 1834, determined to give the railroad a maximum grade of one hundred feet per mile, which was gentler than the grade then in effect on the B & O. Politics changed the route here and there—some communities bought their way to inclusion on the route; others, dominated by canal interests, shunned it—but Wright's engineering standards were upheld. His cost estimates were not: Wright thought the 483-mile route would cost $4,726,260; when the railroad was completed in 1851, it had cost $23,500,000.

And no wonder. To get to the Delaware valley at Port Jervis the railroad had to get across and down the Shawangunk Mountains east of the river. To accomplish this with a gentle and steady grade required a slash through the rocky summit about half a mile long and as much as fifty feet deep. Another cut halfway down the mountain was three-quarters of a mile long and forty feet deep. Along the Delaware River out of Port Jervis, the railroad was forced to the rocky and precipitous southern shore because the Delaware and Hudson Canal had pre-empted the gentler northern bank. At places the workmen had to be suspended in baskets from the tops of steep cliffs while they bored holes in the rock and filled them with blasting powder. To say the job required teamwork is an understatement, for as soon as the men lit the fuses, they had to be hauled up quickly to the top of the cliff.

Four miles from the Susquehanna on their way westward, the railroad builders encountered the deep gorge of Starrucca Creek.

Across it they built a magnificent stone viaduct, consisting of eighteen slender arches 110 feet above the stream. Built to carry the bantam locomotives of its day, it is still there, bearing the weight of 400-ton locomotives and heavy freight cars. Doubtless it caused little joy to the Erie's hard-pressed financiers, for the Starrucca Viaduct had cost them $320,000 to span a mere 1,200-foot distance.

An equally impressive structure, even if short-lived, was the Cascade Bridge, built a few miles to the east of the Starrucca Viaduct. The bridge surmounted a gorge 250 feet wide and 184 feet deep that had walls of solid rock. Completed in the fall of 1848, the bridge was made almost entirely of wood, and its deck rested on top of a graceful arch about 50 feet deep. Tourists loved it, but some passengers feared it, and eventually the railroad abandoned the Cascade Bridge, replacing it with an embankment farther down the ravine.

The Erie builders crossed the gorges and slashed through mountaintops with narrow cuts that became traps for wind and snow. On a branch line from Hornell to Buffalo they built their most difficult bridge: a timber trestle that crossed a chasm 250 feet deep and nearly 900 feet wide. The Portage Bridge (named for a nearby town, not its function) required a million and a half board feet of lumber and one hundred thousand pounds of iron for fastenings. It lasted, a dazzling spectacle for Erie passengers, until it burned down in 1875.

"The pale face has completed a mighty work," said Peter Wilson, a Dartmouth-educated Indian, when the Erie Railroad finally reached Dunkirk in 1851. "He has overcome the most imposing natural barriers; he has pierced the valleys of the Delaware, Susquehanna, Chemung, Allegheny, and levelled the hills which were roamed by my ancestors."

The Erie Railroad was indeed a mighty work, a conquest of the kind of terrain that would not be encountered again until the railroads, more than a decade later, reached the formidable Rocky Mountains in the West. Yet the Appalachians had still not been conquered in all the ways that men knew how. As the railroad work gangs spiked down the last rail of the Erie main line, workmen in western Massachusetts were setting out to conquer Hoosac Mountain—with a tunnel five miles long.

If the Erie, running across rugged and underpopulated terrain, had seemed a foolhardy venture, the Hoosac Tunnel must have struck cynics as the folly of the century. No one had ever dug a tunnel that long. It would have to be carved out of solid rock, under a mountain seventeen hundred feet high, either by brute force or by mechanized methods as yet untried. The tunnel would have to be dug from both sides of the mountain; it would be impossible, some people insisted, to have the two headings meet in the middle. In any case, they pointed out, Boston already had a route to the West: the Boston and Albany Railroad.

But advocates of the tunnel argued that the Boston and Albany, with its steep grades and its circuitous route around Hoosac Mountain twenty miles south of the proposed tunnel, was expensive to operate. Boston was losing business to rival ports. The idea for the tunnel had been proposed as early as 1819 as part of a canal route from Boston to the Hudson. Loammi Baldwin, appointed by the Massachusetts legislature to survey the route in 1825, returned from the proposed site near North Adams bubbling with enthusiasm. "It seems as if the finger of Providence," he once exclaimed, "had pointed out this route from the East to the West." To which a bystander is said to have replied: "It's a great pity the same finger wasn't thrust through the mountain." Baldwin thought the tunnel could be dug for as little as $370,000, certainly—according to his precise calculations—no more than $920,832. The Hoosac Tunnel was eventually to cost ten times that maximum, but in 1826 the Massachusetts legislature was frightened even by Baldwin's estimate, and killed the project.

Almost as soon as the Boston and Albany Railroad completed its route in 1842, however, the idea of the tunnel route was revived, and in 1848 a company was chartered to build it. Still there were those who were sure the tunnel would never be completed. "When the first locomotive wheels roll through the Hoosac Tunnel bore," wrote Oliver Wendell Holmes, "then order your ascension robes." But in 1848 the little railroad company calculated that the tunnel, once it was begun, could be completed in exactly 1,556 working days.

Digging began from both sides of the mountain a few years later. On the east side, an enormous contraption, designed to cut a series of concentric, circular channels up to twenty-four feet in diameter—the full area of the tunnel—was set up and put into operation. The

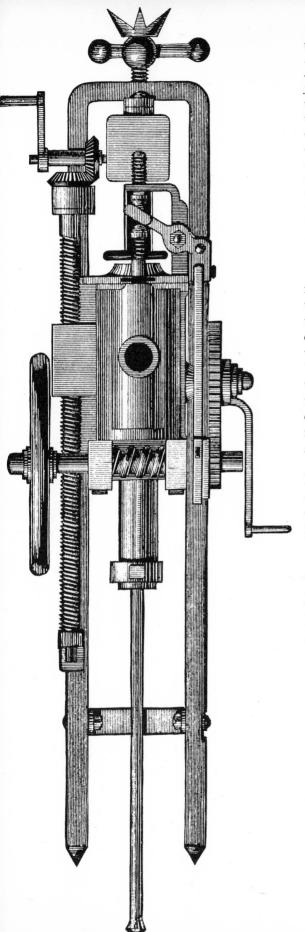

machine whirred and shook and bored a hole ten feet into the mountain before it failed utterly. A few similar leviathans were tried, with equal lack of success. Benjamin Latrobe, reviewing these efforts as consulting engineer in 1862, pointed to the difficulty: "They require the machines to do too much and the powder too little of the work." Blasting was the most efficient way to dig a tunnel through rock; the function of machines, Latrobe indicated, should be to drill holes for the powder.

The 1,556 working days came and went with little achieved. In 1858 Herman Haupt, a distinguished Philadelphia engineer, took charge and began experimenting with mechanical methods, meanwhile continuing to tunnel by the time-honored means of hand-drilling and blasting. Three years later, funds gave out, and Haupt, unjustly charged with corruption and mismanagement, was forced to withdraw. The Commonwealth of Massachusetts took over the ill-starred venture, still only one-fifth completed after ten years' work.

The state commissioners, eager to hurry the project along, sent an engineer to Europe to observe the methods being used in the Mont Cenis Tunnel, then being dug under the Alps between France and Italy. In 1861 Germain Sommeiller, its chief engineer, had introduced a mechanical drill powered by compressed air. It was a clumsy machine, subject to frequent breakdowns, but it had doubled the drilling rate in Mont Cenis. Moreover, by using compressed air, it had distinct advantages over the steam-driven drill then being tried in the Hoosac. Steam had to be piped to the rock face

from a boiler plant outside the tunnel, losing much of its energy en route through radiation of heat and condensation. Miners sweating in the already stuffy atmosphere found that the exhaust from the drills clogged their lungs. Compressed air eliminated these problems.

Since Sommeiller was unwilling to lend his design, the Hoosac engineers set out to build a better one. The first successful model was designed by Charles Burleigh, a mechanical engineer from Fitchburg, Massachusetts. It was put to work in the tunnel in 1866, connected by rubber hose and iron pipe to a compressor designed by the tunnel's chief engineer, Thomas Doane. The piston drove the drill point at about three hundred strokes per minute under an air pressure of forty-two pounds per square inch. Burleigh also built a carriage on which four or more drills were mounted by swivel joints; the carriage ran on rails so that it could be pulled back, out of harm's way, during the blasting stage.

For all the effort toward mechanization, the machine drills were no immediate panacea for the Hoosac's problems. The year they were introduced, 1866, the average monthly progress on the tunnel was less than the year before, and the number of man-days required to remove a cubic yard of rock actually increased—from 3.6 to 4.3.

That same year, however, there was another important innovation: the use of nitroglycerine as an explosive. Doane experimented with the explosive (recently introduced in Europe by Alfred Nobel), and in 1866 he called in a chemist, George M. Mowbray, who had

used the explosive successfully—and prosperously—in Edwin Drake's Pennsylvania oil fields. Mowbray set up a factory to produce nitroglycerine on a ten-acre site near the western end of the tunnel, behind a sign that warded off the curious: "Nitro-Glycerine Works. Dangerous! No Visitors Admitted." Mowbray's product was not only more powerful than the older blasting powder; it lacked the noxious fumes that had plagued workmen in the tunnel. Moreover, nitroglycerine could be poured into deeper holes than the blasting powder, and a single explosion could dislodge far more rock. It was a dangerous substance, but proved safe to handle when kept at a low temperature.

Still the troubles persisted. Most of the rock under Hoosac Mountain was mica schist, which was relatively easy to work, but here and there were veins of quartz, described by one of the engineers as "unyielding as iron." Worse still, the material at the western end of the tunnel was a crumbly, damp rock called "porridge stone," and twenty-five hundred feet of the tunnel had to be lined with brick, sometimes twelve courses thick.

So slow was progress on the western end that the engineers decided to attack from farther along the tunnel route. A vertical shaft, located 3,000 feet to the east of the western portal, was sunk 318 feet to grade level, and the digging commenced in both directions from there. While rock from the eastern heading was being removed by an engine and train of cars, material dug from the western shaft had to be put in cars that were hauled upward by a powerful steam-driven lift. Digging the shaft did not

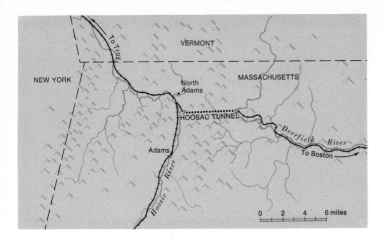

end the troubles on the western end; more than once work had to stop because of flooding from ground water, and could not be resumed until water and debris had been removed.

In 1863, the miners had begun digging another vertical shaft near the center of the mountain, to provide ventilation for the tunnel and offer two more headings to speed up tunneling at grade level. Four years later, when it had been dug only halfway to its intended depth of 1,028 feet, the central shaft became the scene of the Hoosac's worst disaster. A tank of lamp fuel exploded, setting fire to the buildings near the shaft and to combustibles in the shaft itself. Burning timbers, steel drills, pumps, and hoisting cables plummeted down the open shaft, trapping and killing thirteen workmen. Work on the central shaft was halted for a year, while the hole filled nearly to the brim with water; the thirteen bodies were not recovered until the water was pumped out.

The disaster, which cost the Commonwealth of Massachusetts forty thousand dollars, fed the public clamor to bring the Hoosac project to a halt. The tunneling had been so slow and so costly that Francis Bird, leader of the opposition, calculated that a continuation of the project would eventually cost, exclusive of interest, nearly ten million dollars and the tunnel would take more than eighteen years to complete. His estimates may have seemed preposterous at the time, but his cost figure was to prove remarkably—and painfully—correct. Thomas Doane had wearied of the criticism even before the disaster at the central shaft, had quit, and his successor as chief engineer

found it prudent to quit a few months afterward. The state commissioners, also weary of the criticism, sought a private contractor to bring the tunnel quickly to completion.

It was symptomatic of the dire straits and the shoddy politics of the project that the bidders for the contract had to agree to deposit half a million dollars in the Massachusetts state treasury until the project was completed. At the urging of Benjamin Latrobe, Francis and Walter Shanly, Canadian engineers of considerable reputation, submitted a bid and won the contract for $4,594,268. But the Shanly brothers were unable to raise the half-million dollars' deposit, so that a compromise had to be worked out. They agreed to do the first half-million dollars' worth of work without being paid for it until the tunnel was finished. The deadline for completion was March 1, 1874.

When the Shanlys took over at the end of 1868, the tunnel had been dug only about one-third of its total distance. And nothing that had been dug approached the 575-square-foot cross section that would be required for a double-track tunnel more than twenty feet high. The Shanlys had five years in which to accomplish far more than had been done in the preceding fifteen.

To increase the capacity of the drills, they brought in large air compressors. To cope with the ground water leaking into the tunnel (in places, at the rate of three thousand gallons an hour), they brought in heavier pumps. They put seven hundred men to work—Cornish miners, French Canadians, a sprinkling of Germans, Danes, and Irishmen—in three

*The Hoosac Tunnel had to be bored through rocks of varying hardness. Mica schist, the most prevalent rock, was easy to work, but in the eastern half there were frequent bands of very hard quartz, and in the west, veins of granitic gneiss. But the most troublesome rock was the soft "demoralized" schist at the western end. There the tunnel was lined with brick to prevent collapse, and the west portal (below) was finished off with stone arching.*

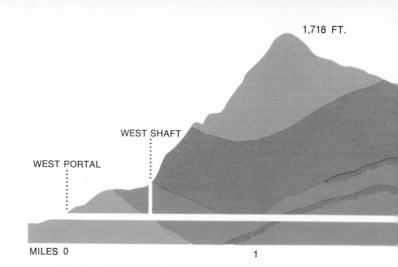

1,718 FT.

WEST SHAFT

WEST PORTAL

MILES 0                    1

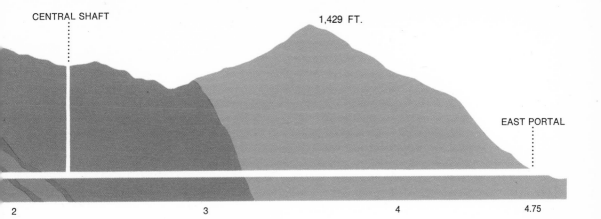

CENTRAL SHAFT

1,429 FT.

EAST PORTAL

2    3    4    4.75

shifts around the clock, closing down only on Sundays. By the end of their first year, the Shanlys had advanced the tunnel another 1,514 feet. They had also run through the first half-million dollars, some of it just to repair heartbreaking setbacks. On Saturday night, October 2, 1869, it began to rain. It was raining at midnight on Sunday when the week's first shift of workmen entered the tunnel, and it continued to rain throughout the next day. On Monday afternoon a brook near the western end broke through its embankment and the water came rushing into the tunnel. By the time the last of the hundred workmen were hauled up through the western shaft, the water had risen to within eighteen inches of the roof of the tunnel. Much of the brickwork was weakened and dislodged, and the state held the Shanly brothers financially responsible for its repair, even though at the time of their contract that section of the tunnel was considered completed. At the eastern end of the tunnel, railroad track was washed away, and the trains that had hauled workmen and supplies to the site were out of commission for nine months.

In the summer of 1870, the Shanlys completed the digging of the central shaft. As a precaution against a repeat of the disaster there, they had chiseled notches in the rock lining of the shaft at regular intervals, into which they lodged timbers to support a sturdy platform at each of these levels. Eventually there were sixty-two such platforms along the 1,028-foot shaft. To keep the bottom of this great pit reasonably dry required a relay of eight pumps spaced throughout the shaft and operated continuously to discharge 214 gallons of water per minute. To get men and materials up and down the shaft, Frank Shanly devised a steam-powered elevator that was much like the one Elisha Otis had patented in 1861 but operating through a far greater distance than had hitherto been tried. Digging an oval-shaped hole twenty-seven feet by fifteen feet and nearly as deep as the Empire State Building is tall was an impressive achievement. But it was also costly and, in the end, accounted for just 15 per cent of the horizontal digging of the tunnel.

The more remarkable accomplishment at the central shaft was the solving of the trickiest business of all tunnel-digging: keeping the excavation correctly lined up so that headings from opposite directions will meet up. In the Hoosac Tunnel, since the digging from the central shaft was outward in two directions (to meet the headings from both east and west), the alignment problem had to be solved not once but twice. And it was, with considerable precision. When the tunnelers broke through in one direction in 1872 and then in the other in 1874, the error in alignment, horizontally and vertically, was in each case only a fraction of an inch. The Mont Cenis Tunnel, which was three miles longer than the Hoosac and was completed four years earlier, had an error in alignment of half a yard.

Those who had preceded the Shanlys as Hoosac engineers had, of course, coped with the alignment problem to give direction to the east and west headings and to locate the central and western shafts. Hoosac Mountain had two humps, like an Asiatic camel, and on each

*To provide ventilation for the tunnel and with the hope of speeding up the digging, the engineers began sinking the central shaft in 1863. Their work went slowly, and two years later they calculated that each foot of progress was costing 57 man-days of labor. Not until 1870 did the shaft reach grade level, and the horizontal digging from there amounted to only 3,619 linear feet—about 15 per cent of the tunnel's total length.*

of these summits the engineers erected masonry towers, topped by fifteen-foot iron poles. These marked the line of the tunnel route but, since no one at either foot of the mountain could see both poles, two more had to be erected on peaks to the east and west of Hoosac Mountain, in line with the original pair.

At each portal, then, the surveyors had two coordinate points with which to line up their transit instruments and determine the direction of digging. As the digging progressed, they drove wooden pegs into the ceiling of the tunnel every two dozen feet, hung plumb lines from them, and used these as reference points for the alignment.

The problem of determining this line for the digging from the central shaft proved infinitely more difficult. The shaft was only twenty-five feet wide, and if either of the coordinate points within this distance were off by a fraction of an inch, digging would be set wildly off course. The line, of course, had first to be determined from the mountaintop, using the original pair of iron poles, and then somehow conveyed accurately down the thousand-foot shaft.

The surveyors could not work on the platform directly over the shaft because vibrations from the pumps and elevator set their instruments ajar. So they built two masonry piers along the axis of the tunnel, each about twenty-five feet from the shaft. On top of each pier they mounted an adjustable iron block containing a thin vertical slit. The slits were used for sighting the alignment. When the surveyors had completed the adjustment of the slits, a pair of piano wires, one-twentieth of an inch

apart, were stretched tautly from one pier to the other through the slits. Two plumb lines, hanging between the piano wires and positioned twenty-three feet apart, had to be encased in wooden flues the full distance down the shaft, and their fifteen-pound plummets at the bottom suspended in buckets of water to subdue vibrations. Even then, the plumb lines oscillated an intolerable one-hundredth of an inch, and the surveyors had to determine the true line by taking the average of several hundred observations.

The surveyors also had to be careful to maintain a constant grade, twenty-six feet to the mile sloping downward from the center in both directions to allow the tunnel to drain itself of water that seeped in. Soon after the tunnel was completed, a newspaper reported that water was flowing through the drain at the western end at the rate of four hundred gallons a minute. The ever-resourceful Yankees who ran the explosives factory nearby were using it as a power source.

But until the tunnel was opened to daylight, there could be no internal natural drainage and the pumps worked continuously. The residents of nearby North Adams got used to the unending din of the pumps and the compressors, and the frequent loud reports from exploding rock. By 1872, the Shanly brothers had achieved a pace far in excess of the rate prescribed by their contract. They prudently ignored the demands of the state commissioners for faster progress westward from the central shaft, since the wet rock on that side overtaxed the pumps, and from time to time

*The Hoosac Tunnel was a proving ground for modern hard-rock tunneling techniques, and one of the most important was the use of nitroglycerine, forerunner of dynamite. It was twice as potent as the blasting powder formerly used, and it left no noxious fumes in the wake of an explosion. One annoying result went unchanged, however; blasting tended to open up new sources of seeping ground water, and at times workmen had to endure downpours (right).*

they had to use the elevator for bailing out water. By concentrating on the eastern headings, the Shanlys were able to open that section on December 12, 1872. For the next two years they fought against the dripping rock under the western side of the mountain. On the afternoon of Thanksgiving Day, 1874, only thirteen feet of rock stood between the two western headings. The previous day a hole two inches wide had been bored through the rock, and now electric wires were passed through the hole so that, for dramatic effect, the rock could be blasted from both sides simultaneously. Newsmen crouched behind barriers a safe distance away as George Mowbray, the chemist, packed a charge of seventy pounds of nitroglycerine. Walter Shanly fired the battery that sent thunder rolling through the tunnel and hurled rock against the wooden barriers. When the debris and dust had settled, a crowd surged forward, but the workmen insisted that Walter Shanly be the first to go through the opening. Shanly gallantly passed the honor to Robert Johnson, head of the state commissioners.

Track still had to be laid, and the following year it was decided another eighty-five hundred feet of tunnel should be lined with brick. But that November day of 1874 marked the conquest of Hoosac Mountain. A million tons of rock had been removed to make a tunnel five miles long, and twenty million bricks had been put in to shore it up. The digging had consumed a half-million pounds of nitroglycerine and an endless number of drill points. In twenty years of construction, 195 men had lost their lives in explosions, subterranean floods,

and the crush of fallen timbers. A decade after it was finished, the state government was still allocating nearly half of its revenue to pay off Hoosac Tunnel debts. In 1887 they sold it to private interests.

The Hoosac Tunnel was not one of railroading's greatest achievements. It opened a route for the Troy and Greenfield Railroad that was only a few miles and a few minutes shorter than the Boston and Albany route. It was, of course, put to good use, and it spurred a healthy competition between the two railroads. In the 1920's, when the tunnel belonged to the Boston and Maine, and indeed was its lifeline, more than ninety trains a day passed through it. But the last passenger train entered the tunnel in 1958, and today only a dozen freights a day pass through it. There is a single set of tracks where once there were two. Inspectors, who used to be on duty around the clock, now walk the tunnel only twice a week. The ties are rotting and the walls are crumbling, but no one bothers to repair them.

The significance of the Hoosac Tunnel is to be found, not in its service to a railroad, but in what it did for the technology of tunneling. It brought it from a crude, muscle-powered art to a highly mechanized, efficient process. The techniques of hard-rock tunneling still being used, the powerful pneumatic drills and explosives, all derive from the Hoosac experience. While the tunnel was being dug, at a high cost of money and lives, its critics called it a devouring Minotaur. The Minotaur, it will be recalled, was slain by a mighty warrior. The Hoosac was conquered by man's inventiveness.

The pace quickened in the final years of digging as 1,000 men toiled in eight-hour shifts around the clock. About half of the time was devoted to drilling, the rest to moving the drills out of the way, setting the explosives, and clearing away the blasted rock. On a good day, six drilling machines would be at work on a heading, and in eight hours' time they would drill 12 holes 12 feet long. (In the process, drill points had to be changed 60 times.) There were setbacks, of course—drills breaking, pumps clogging, air hoses bursting—and accidents: in two decades of digging 195 men lost their lives in the Hoosac. The tunnel cost $10,000,000— almost $400 per linear foot. In the 1880's it had two tracks busily carrying traffic, but now it resembles the tunnel seen in this earlier photograph; a single track runs down the center line, so that today's taller loads can pass through.

# AND THEN
# CAME STEEL

In 1850 America had about nine thousand miles of railroad track, most of it concentrated in the Northeast. Within a decade the figure had tripled, and the area of intense activity extended all the way to the Mississippi. Railroads were the chief stimulus to the economic development of the Midwest—populating towns, subsidizing businesses, promoting the settlement of homesteads, openly influencing legislation in state after state.

When the outbreak of the Civil War in 1861 interrupted this feverish building boom, northern railroad magnates revived the idea, first mentioned in the 1840's, of a transcontinental railroad that would link the Midwest with the Pacific Coast. The suggestion was well received in Washington. A physical link between the West Coast states and the rest of the Union would strengthen a rather tenuous ideological bond. President Lincoln lent his support and in 1862 Congress passed the Pacific Railway Act, which chartered the Union Pacific and Central Pacific railroads, granting them federal aid in both money and land for the construction of a cross-country line. The Union Pacific began laying track at Omaha, Nebraska, and headed westward toward the Rockies, while the Central Pacific set out eastward from Sacramento, California.

The route of the Union Pacific followed the level valley of the Platte River. Its work gangs were hampered but not halted by bands of Indian warriors trying desperately to save their hunting grounds from the invasion of the iron horse. The mountainous course of the Central Pacific, in contrast, was almost all natural ob-

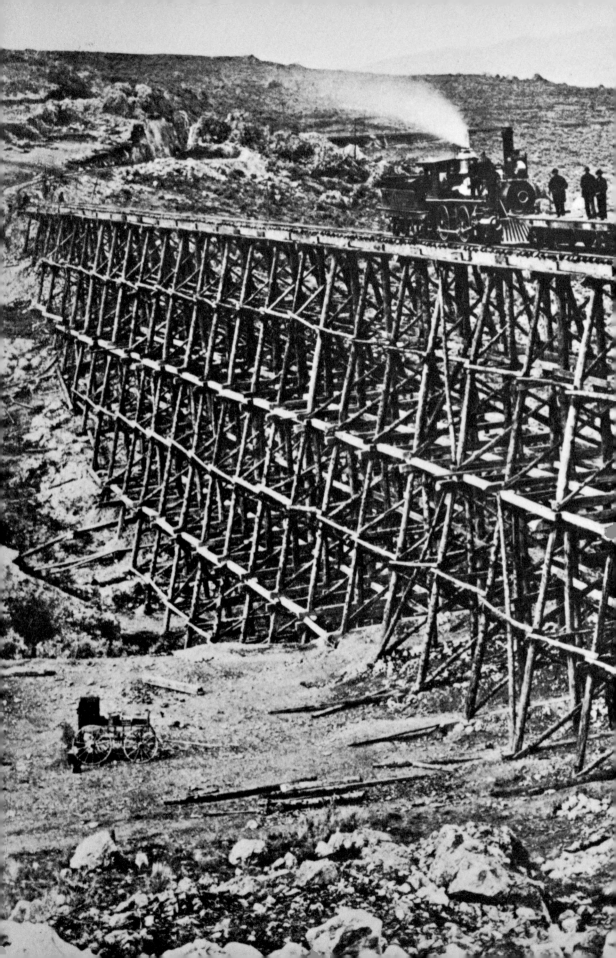

stacle. Mile after mile of track had to be laid on man-made ledges blasted out of the Sierra slopes, and the most extensive series of bridges and tunnels in the world was required to fill in the gaps.

Despite the barriers and the hardships, the largely Irish crew of the Union Pacific and largely Chinese crew of the Central Pacific pushed steadily toward one another. So eager were the rival companies to secure the generous land grants and subsidies that accompanied each mile of track, that violent battles broke out as the track-laying teams moved closer. To eliminate the constant threat of sabotage, Congress hastily set the final meeting place in advance.

On May 10, 1869, the two single tracks were joined by a golden spike at Promontory Point in the Utah desert. Eastern trains had already reached Omaha, terminus of the Union Pacific, so there was at last a transcontinental railroad. The journey from coast to coast could be made in a week.

The coming of the transcontinental railroad changed the entire direction of the nation's growth. Wharves and waterways became less crucial to a town's expansion than the crisscrossing of train tracks; possession of both ensured a city's future. Chicago had one railroad terminal and thirty thousand residents in 1852; by 1869 it was a city of three hundred thousand people, a city virtually created by the railroads.

As Chicago grew, its arch rival, St. Louis, on the Mississippi, fell behind in the struggle for domination of the Midwest. At first, the citi-

*The first long-span truss bridge was built over the Ohio River at Steubenville, in 1864. Engineer for the 320-foot iron span was J. H. Linville, who later became president of the Keystone Bridge Company. He used a form of Whipple truss with ornate cylindrical posts for support. The posts and all compression members were cast, while the diagonal braces and other tension members used wrought iron, which has greater tensile strength.*

zens of St. Louis, loyal to the river that had made their city great, were confident that its north-south trade would complement, rather than compete with, the predominantly east-west traffic of the trains. The state of Missouri had nearly a thousand miles of railroad track west of the Mississippi, but eastern cargoes and cars had to cross the river by ferry in order to use it. As transcontinental traffic grew, it naturally tended to use the only bridges across the Mississippi, all built farther north (where the river was shallower and narrower than at St. Louis) by railroads whose terminal was in Chicago.

It was inevitable that a suitable crossing would be devised to link St. Louis with the East, but the Mississippi stretched for fifteen hundred feet between the city's wharves and those of East St. Louis, Illinois, on the opposite bank. Its waters were liable to sudden, spectacular flooding and its navigable channels shifted constantly. It was indeed a monumental obstacle. A bridge at St. Louis would take more time, more money, and more thinking than bridge builders had so far expended on any of their structures.

For years railroad magnates and their allies in the bridge-building business had settled for the cheapest rather than the strongest bridges; speed of construction was their chief interest. This policy was already reaping a bitter harvest as existing bridge technology began baring its weaknesses. Highways as well as railroads had their share of disasters, which mounted steadily in the 50's and 60's. In the decade between 1870 and 1880 bridges collapsed at the rate of forty a year. Even at this date, more than half of them were timber spans.

One of the worst failures—and one of the worst railroad disasters of the nineteenth century—took place on a bridge spanning a deep gorge at Ashtabula, Ohio. Erected in 1865, it was a Howe truss similar to many earlier Howe trusses, except that cast iron had entirely replaced the timber members. The original design had been modified by Amasa Stone, a well-known bridge builder who was also president of the railroad concerned, the Lake Shore and Michigan Southern. On December 29, 1876, an eleven-car train drawn by two locomotives began to cross the Ashtabula bridge at fifteen miles an hour, westbound. Snow was still pelting down from a recent blizzard. As the engineer of the first locomotive reached the center of the 165-foot span, he felt the bridge begin to sink. Opening the throttle to its widest, he managed to get his own engine safely across; but the second locomotive and all the cars behind went down into the icy waters. Eighty lives were lost.

The Ashtabula tragedy aroused a storm of protest. At first, the tendency was to assume that the bridge had been cheaply built and that no inspections had been made. But when investigating committees discovered that the bridge had cost seventy-five thousand dollars (which made it relatively expensive for its time) and had in fact been inspected regularly, the blame shifted to the engineer responsible for those inspections. Although he had carried them out conscientiously, the unfortunate man was so distressed by the charges that he com-

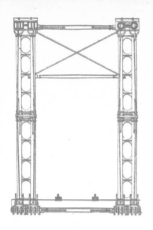
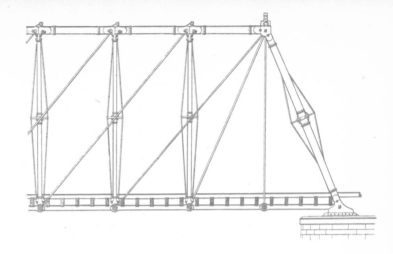

mitted suicide. The attack was then turned upon Stone himself, and both he and his design were eventually condemned by the American Society of Civil Engineers.

Curiously, no one could establish exactly why the bridge had fallen. The soundest theory was that some cars had become derailed, perhaps just before reaching the bridge. As the derailed metal wheels struck the flooring, the floor beams began to give way, pulling both lines of trussing inward at the top. The trusses, which had not been designed for such a strain, collapsed. Although under similar circumstances almost any truss of the time would have fallen in, Stone was disgraced.

The Ashtabula disaster simply highlighted a problem that everyone knew existed. Even the resulting public clamor did not generate sufficient action to reduce the rate of bridge failures: in the decade that followed, some two hundred bridges collapsed. A few state legislatures established railroad commissions that were empowered, supposedly, to set safety standards, dictate specifications, oversee construction, and make periodic inspections, but the railroad men and bridge builders were too powerful to tolerate any real restrictions.

The physical character of the truss had attracted the interest of a growing number of business and financial operators in the 1860's. Since the truss's small, similar members were easy to standardize and mass-produce, a handful of bridge companies grew up, patented their own variations on the basic truss designs, and quickly dominated the rapidly expanding market for railroad and highway bridges. As with

any competitive business, profit depended on the speed and economy of operations.

As the record of disasters mounted, the magnates began to realize that the losses involved were much greater than the profits to be made out of building replacements. Belatedly recognizing the need to assure public safety, they began commissioning bridges made from wrought iron, with strong, riveted joints replacing pin connections, which were more vulnerable to stress. But the unimaginative years had left a void. Good bridges cost money and engineers had grown too accustomed to letting economy be their decision-maker.

Yet the material they needed to transform the craft of bridge-building into a science was already at hand. In 1855, the English scientist Henry Bessemer had invented a practical way to make steel, the most versatile of metals—strong yet flexible, hard yet resilient. Once adapted to the particular type of iron ore most common in the United States, Bessemer's method became cheap as well as practical. Using steel, a number of creative Americans were to end the infancy of the bridge.

Ironically, on the stormy December night when the iron truss at Ashtabula tumbled headlong into the ravine, a bridge constructed chiefly of steel had already been in existence for two and a half years. It still stands today with its two roadways, supported by three massive arches, carrying road and rail traffic across the Mississippi as reliably as on the day it was opened in 1874. Yet the man who undertook to span America's mightiest river and give St. Louis its sorely needed link with the

East had never before built a bridge. He lacked any formal training in engineering; indeed, he had never finished high school.

Fortunately for St. Louis, the risk involved in employing James Buchanan Eads turned out to be a stroke of brilliance. He was a natural engineering genius, whose knowledge of the Mississippi matched his vision of the bridge he proposed to build across it. Still more important, no amount of opposition—and he had plenty—could daunt his will to succeed.

James Eads, born in Indiana in 1820, made a spectacular arrival in St. Louis aboard a steamboat that erupted in flames just before reaching the dock. Eads, then a boy of thirteen, and his mother and sisters lost everything they owned in the fire, but the mother managed to support them all by taking in boarders, while her son peddled apples in the street. He soon found more permanent employment as a clerk in a grocery store, where he spent a typical future-great-American's youth working industriously and being allowed the run of his employer's excellent library above the shop. By the time he quit, at the age of eighteen, to take a clerk's post on a Mississippi steamboat, James Eads had laid the foundations of a remarkable private education.

In the three years as a steamboat clerk he grew to know the river well and to wonder more and more at the quantity of wrecks that took place as boats struck snags or went aground on its sand banks. When he asked how the drowned vessels and their cargoes were salvaged, Eads discovered that no proper salvaging operation existed on the Mississippi.

As he was to do many times in his life, he set out to tackle a problem others were quite content to live with.

Before he was twenty-two, Eads conceived of a twin-hulled vessel equipped with derricks and pumps to raise sunken cargoes from the river bottom. He called it the Submarine (referring to its purpose—it did not submerge) and in 1842 he found himself two partners with the capital to go into business. He improvised a diving bell that would enable a diver with an air pump and proper equipment—most frequently it was to be Eads himself—to spend hour after hour on the river bed. Word was scarcely out about his new operation when he had more business than he could handle. The money rolled in and Eads and his partners grew rich.

In 1845 Eads sold out his interest in order to open a glass-manufacturing plant. With typical diligence, he visited glass factories in the East and studied their processes carefully before embarking on the new business. He almost succeeded but was wiped out by the Mexican War before he could get on his feet. With a debt of twenty-five thousand dollars to liquidate, all his savings gone, and a family to support, James Eads borrowed fifteen hundred dollars to buy back a share in the Submarine, and went back to the salvage business as a diver. Within ten years he and his partner had a fleet of Submarines and a joint fortune of more than half a million dollars.

At the outbreak of the Civil War, Eads traveled to Washington to try to convince the government that the Union needed a fleet of

In 1879 American engineers were appalled by a bridge disaster in Britain, which then led the world in industrial design. Under gale-force winds the center spans of a new iron bridge across the Firth of Tay collapsed into the sea, along with a train carrying 75 people. All were lost and investigators blamed the bridge's poor design and materials. Both Britain and America soon began building bridges that were made entirely out of steel.

*Iron has an innate tendency
to rust and deteriorate, and
the pin-connected joints that
were traditionally used on iron
bridges could be dangerously
weakened when they
rusted solid in their sockets.
Though stronger than iron, steel
is even more liable to rust.
Builders using steel therefore
switched to riveted joints,
which were both rigid and
resistant. After half a century
of exposure, this specimen
is still eminently reliable.*

ironclad gunboats on the Mississippi to keep
the waterway open and its border-state banks
in northern hands. In August, 1861, he signed a
government contract by which he bound himself to deliver seven 600-ton armor-plated vessels in the incredibly short space of sixty-five
days. Despite chaotic wartime conditions, he
got mills and machine shops open in state after
state, and within two weeks he had four
thousand men working around the clock, seven
days a week. Within forty-five days the first
gunboat was ready and Eads's tornado of activity actually succeeded in completing the
fleet in December, 1861, with the addition of
an eighth vessel, one of his own Submarines,
heavily armored.

By the time the war was over, Eads had
built fourteen ironclads, converted seven
transports into light "tinclads," designed four
heavy mortar boats, and patented several ord-
nance inventions that strikingly foreshadowed
the equipment to be used by modern armored
fleets. Though his health had broken down under the strain, his versatile mind was already
busy with fresh schemes.

The coming of peace meant that St. Louis
must instantly get to work on building a railroad bridge across the Mississippi, or forever
relinquish its hopes of playing a significant
part in the development of the western fron-
tier. Before the war, such able bridge engineers
as Charles Ellet and John Roebling had submitted designs for suspension bridges to be
mounted on piles sunk in the river bed. The
city council had rejected them on grounds of
cost and of impracticality.

To Eads, however, the idea of any bridge
supported on piles was truly impracticable.
The Mississippi flows past St. Louis at about
225,000 cubic feet of water per second, the vol-
ume and speed increasing to about 1,000,000
cubic feet at high water. Eads knew, as did no
other man, what effect this had upon the river
bottom. Exploring the river bed in his diving
bell during a flood, he had found it "for at least
three feet in depth, a moving mass, and so un-
stable that, in endeavoring to find a footing on
it . . . I could feel, although standing erect, the
sand rushing past my hands, driven by a current apparently as rapid as that at the surface." An enduring bridge over such a river
had to have its foundations on bedrock. And at
St. Louis, bedrock was anywhere from forty to
one hundred feet below the surface of the turbulent Mississippi.

In 1866 the St. Louis and Illinois Bridge
Company, which had already won charters
from the states of Missouri and Illinois em-
powering it to build a bridge, obtained the
franchise from Congress that was necessary for
any proposal to span a navigable river. The
company still faced strong opposition, however, from competing ferryboat operators,
steamboat companies, and the Chicago railroads. The most effective of these were the railroad men, who persuaded the Illinois legislature to charter another bridge company,
headed by a Chicago contractor.

The outraged St. Louis concern retorted
swiftly by electing James Eads as their chief
engineer, and in March, 1867, he presented his
preliminary plans. They called for a handsome

triple-span arch, each span over five hundred feet long, supported by abutments and two piers, all of stone, sunk to bedrock. The arches would be built of steel, which had never been used before as principal material for a bridge superstructure. No previous arch or even truss spans five hundred feet long were in existence. Nowhere had piers been built from so deep a river foundation. Feeling that Eads might appreciate assistance from an experienced bridge engineer, the St. Louis company asked J. H. Linville, president of the Keystone Bridge Company of Pittsburgh, to review the plan. But Linville was outraged. "I cannot consent to imperil my reputation by appearing to encourage or approve its adoption," he wrote, courteously submitting a substitute of his own design, an iron truss.

Impressed by Eads's infectious confidence, the St. Louis company asked him to proceed with his plans without a consulting engineer. This gave the Illinois company a great propaganda aid. A convention of twenty-seven engineers was promptly summoned, which unanimously condemned the steel-arch concept. On the day before the convention opened, Eads quietly began the construction of his west abutment at a busy spot in the center of the St. Louis water front.

Aware that the scrap and waste of sixty years had accumulated on the river bed, Eads planned to cut a cleft in the junk into which thick pointed boards of sheet piling could be forced to form a cofferdam. (A cofferdam is a double wall of sheet piling that is built up all around the pier site to a point well above water

level. The water within is then pumped out so that the pier foundation can be laid in the drained area.) But even Eads had not anticipated the mass of debris at the river bottom. It took a total of six months to complete the ordinarily routine business of building the dam, and then the Mississippi waters rose and flooded it from the top, delaying the work of laying the pier masonry for another two months. And this west abutment, based just forty feet below the surface of the water, was supposed to be the easiest to sink of the four foundations.

The one encouraging development was the opening of negotiations between the competing Illinois and Missouri bridge-building companies, which ended in a merger of the two and the adoption of Eads's design, 500-foot spans and all.

In the fall of 1868, Eads became seriously ill and had to go abroad to convalesce. In France, he visited a bridge site where piers were being sunk by means of the recently invented pneumatic caisson. This was a watertight cylinder with a floorless chamber at the bottom that could be submerged to the bed of the river and used instead of a cofferdam in deep water. Compressed air pumped into the chamber enabled it to resist the water pressure even at great depths and provided ventilation for men inside, whose job it was to excavate ever deeper into the river bed. Above the water level, meanwhile, other workers were laying course after course of the masonry pier on top of the chamber roof. The increasing weight kept the cylinder slowly sinking so that the excavators

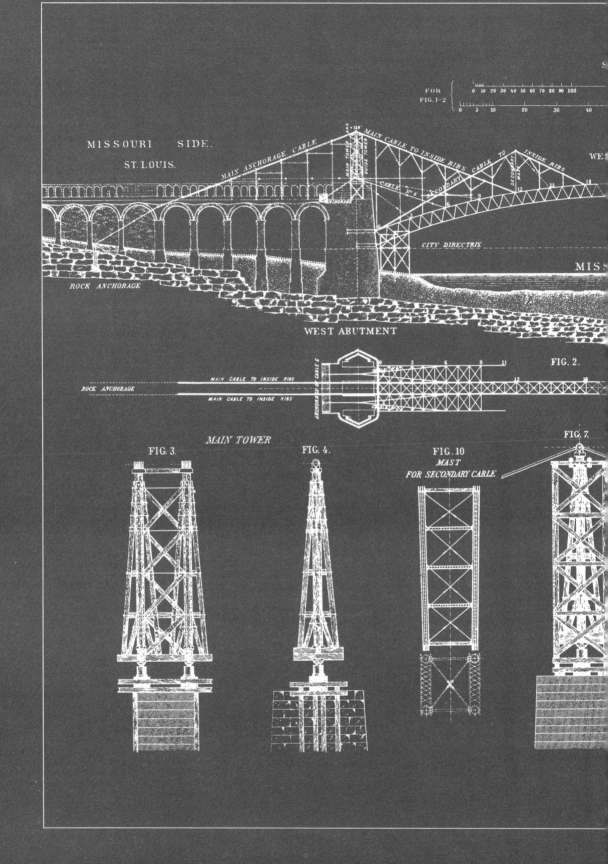

MISSOURI SIDE.

ST. LOUIS.

MAIN ANCHORAGE CABLE

MAIN CABLE TO INSIDE RIBS

MAIN TOWER

GUIDE TOWER

MAIN GUIDE CABLE

SECONDARY CABLE TO INSIDE RIBS

WES

CABLE N° 6

ANCHORAGE

SECONDARY MAST

INSIDE RIBS

CITY DIRECTRIX

MISS

ROCK ANCHORAGE

WEST ABUTMENT

FOR
FIG. 1-2

0 10 20 30 40 50 60 70 80 90 100

0    5    10         20         30         40

MAIN CABLE TO INSIDE RIBS

ROCK ANCHORAGE

MAIN CABLE TO INSIDE RIBS

ANCHORAGE OF CABLE 6

FIG. 2.

MAIN TOWER

FIG. 3.

FIG. 4.

FIG. 10
MAST
FOR SECONDARY CABLE

FIG. 7.

200     250     300 FEET

70    80    90    100 METRES

SECONDARY CABLE  TO INSIDE  MAIN CABLE TO INSIDE RIBS * 130'5  MAIN CABLE TO INSIDE RIBS  TO  INSIDE RIBS.

CENTER SPAN

520'

closing tube

closing tube

CITY DIRECTRIX

RIVER    BARGE

WEST PIER

DOTTED LINES IN FIG.1 REPRESENT

AUXILIARY CABLES.

FIG. 8.

GUIDE TOWER
FIG. 5.

FIG. 9.

FIG. 6.

FOR
FIG. 3 - 10

10  5  0    10    20    30    40    50    60  FEET

0 1 2 3 4 5 6 7 8 9 10    20  METRES

worked in a completely watertight compartment. Once bedrock was reached, the working chamber and its access stairway would be filled with concrete to become the base and central core of the pier.

Although the caisson method had never been used to sink foundations of the depth Eads was planning, he felt he had found the solution to his problems. Deciding to try the new method out by sinking the two shallower piers first and leaving the difficult east abutment until last, he hurried home to design his caissons. The change of method involved altering all his plans and machinery as well as building two box-shaped structures eighty-two feet long. By September, 1869, the indefatigable Eads had fifteen hundred men at work.

That October the east pier caisson was floated into position and lowered until it reached sand fourteen feet down. Then the men soon to be known as sand hogs descended a spiral stairway to the air locks that sealed off the compressed-air chamber. They paused in the locks while the pressure was raised to equal that in the pressurized section, then opened the doors and entered the low-roofed working chamber. Eads had invented water-operated sand pumps that removed the sand they shoveled from the chamber, blowing it out through exhaust pipes in the top of the caisson. Shifts of sand hogs, breathing compressed air, worked around the clock at excavating, while the masonry pier grew steadily above them.

All winter the Eads crew, as determined as their tough, respected boss, worked through icy storms and bitter cold. The men were twice

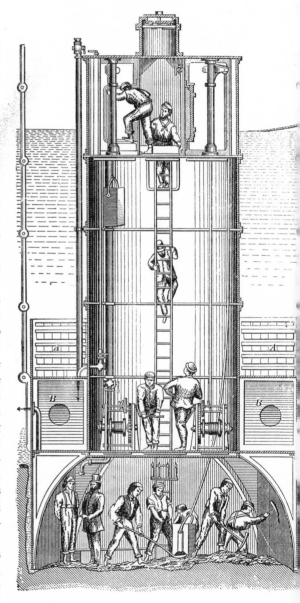

marooned at the pier because ice blocked the way to relief shifts and supplies. But the work continued without a break, and it was not until spring that the real trouble began.

As the caisson inched deeper, air pressure increased—twenty pounds to the square inch, twenty-two, twenty-five, thirty. The trouble hardly seemed serious and in fact did not occur until after the men left the caisson: then, on the way home, a brief, sharp pain in the stomach, a split-second's paralysis. The workers had their own way of coping with these minor symptoms: they wore zinc or silver bracelets and anklets and smeared themselves with "Abolition Oil." They called the ailment the bends, after the position induced by the pains. At a depth of seventy-six feet, when the air pressure had risen to thirty-two, the symptoms were minor no longer. One worker's pains became so agonizing that he had to be hospitalized.

Eads ordered that only men in good physical condition should work in the compressed-air chamber, reduced the shifts to two hours, and abolished night work altogether. Incidents of the bends became fewer as the caisson sank deeper and hit bedrock on February 28, 1870, ninety-three and a half feet below the surface of the water.

Then the spring thaw brought floodwater down the Mississippi. The water level rose, and with it the need to increase air pressure in the chamber. At forty-four pounds the first death occurred. Five more deaths followed in the next few days. Work was now in full swing at the west pier, which hit bedrock seventy-eight feet down on April 1, 1870. There, too, men

were struck down. That November work began on the east abutment, where Eads, striving to prevent "caisson disease," had installed new lighting, an elevator to transport the men, and a room where they could rest during breaks. The bends continued to claim victims.

Finally, Eads's own doctor, whom he had called in to treat the afflicted, was stricken as he left the west pier caisson. He recovered, however, and as he did so, he realized that he had spent only three minutes in the air lock between the work chamber and normal atmosphere. At once he ordered the decompression rate in the air lock of the east abutment reduced to six pounds a minute—still not slow enough by modern standards of one pound per minute. There were still a few cases of the bends, and one death. But compared with the toll on the piers—ninety-one victims, of whom thirteen died, and two were crippled for life— the results were remarkable.

In other areas the Eads Bridge's safety record was excellent. The designer's foresight in building huge breakwaters upstream paid off when a giant ice gorge ripped down the river on Christmas, 1870, and was successfully turned aside. The following March the worst tornado St. Louis had ever known struck the east abutment, snapping timbers and cables, and knocking out every engine and pump on the job. One man was killed and several injured, but the rest of the crew managed to repair the damage and within three weeks the east abutment stood complete, on a base 136 feet below high-water level. The labor of laying the four foundations had taken three and a half years.

Eads's greatest foresight was his insistence that he set the specifications for the steel to be used in the bridge members. All the major bridge companies wanted the job of building the great tubular steel arches, but all were shocked, and some baffled, by Eads's demands. Their workmen were awkward at handling the unfamiliar material, and delays cost money. To add insult to injury, Eads had a specially built testing machine installed in his office, and firmly rejected any metal that failed to match his original specifications.

The obvious choice to build the superstructure was the Keystone Bridge Company, the foremost in the country. Its president, J. H. Linville, did not like the bridge any better than he had in 1867. But Keystone's vice president, an ambitious young Scotsman named Andrew Carnegie, persuaded Linville early in 1870 to bid for the major construction work. Carnegie was both financially and practically involved with the Eads Bridge. His career as a money-maker, by his own admission, was founded on a daring sale of four million dollars of the bridge's bonds to the financier Junius Morgan, in London. Carnegie himself soon became a bondholder and a director of the bridge company. Vital, charming, and unscrupulous, the Scotsman found that Eads was one man he could not get around.

When Keystone's subcontractor delayed in delivering the steel tubes that would be coupled together to form the arch ribs, Eads bought elsewhere, at a higher price. The infuriated Carnegie, at a bondholders' meeting, demanded that an "experienced engineer"—and

of course he meant Linville—be asked to study the plans to find ways of cutting expenses. To Carnegie's astonishment, Eads agreed. James Laurie, an experienced and disinterested engineer, was commissioned to look over the plans. He had not a fault to find.

Despite continuing difficulties and steadily mounting costs, by the spring of 1873 Eads was ready to raise the arches. Normally, arches are erected over a temporary timber scaffolding that stretches from pier to pier, called centering (as distinct from the scaffolding used to erect a level span, which is called falsework). But Eads could not erect centering in the Mississippi River. His solution was ingeniously simple in theory, but required yet another novel feat of engineering. He would build wooden towers on top of the abutments and piers and cantilever the steel arches out from the stone masonry. As they spread outward they would be held up by suspension wires extending to the towers. Once the arches were joined, they would become self-sustaining, and the cables could be removed.

Gradually the arches spread outward over the river and in September, 1873, it was time to close the first span, a difficult task that the Keystone Company left entirely to the bridge experts. As the half-ribs expanded and contracted, depending on the sun's heat, their position varied constantly. The solution, devised by Eads, was to screw adjustable plugs inside the final tubes of each rib, extending them to whatever degree was required at the time they were actually closed.

By January, 1874, all three arches were

closed and the chief remaining task was the laying of the dual roadbeds. Eads, visiting New York to reassure bondholders there that the bridge was at last nearly complete, was awakened the night before the meeting by a bellboy bearing a telegram. The wire, from an assistant in St. Louis, told him that cracks were appearing in the arch ribs.

Eads did not panic. He thought. And the answer eventually came, without his looking at the bridge, without any further communication about its condition. He wired back, telling his aide to loosen the temporary cables. They were, he had realized, contracting because of the cold weather and pulling the arches in different directions. There was nothing wrong with the Eads Bridge and Eads knew it.

On May 24, 1874, pedestrians crossed for the first time. Vehicles rolled over on June 3. Several days later a locomotive crossed on the lower roadbed. On July 2, fourteen locomotives, crammed with passengers and hauling brim-filled coal cars, crossed back and forth in every possible combination. One nervous engineer even had his engine in reverse, but was pulled across nevertheless by the others. Eads had hoped to have every inch of bridge loaded with steam locomotives at once, but fourteen were all he could borrow.

At its formal opening two days later, the bridge displayed a simple plaque: "The Mississippi discovered by Marquette, 1673; spanned by Captain Eads, 1874."

The building of the Eads Bridge was a true landmark in American engineering. The specification of parts rapidly became expected and accepted by industry. The bad old practice of adapting existing designs and materials gave way to the commissioning of qualified and experienced engineers, who built bridges scientifically designed to meet the individual needs of the terrain and type of traffic. Most important of all, Eads's inspired handling of steel guaranteed its acceptance as the structural material of the future. Four years after the St. Louis bridge was completed, General William Sooy Smith built the first *all*-steel bridge to be erected in America at Glasgow, Missouri. The 1,570-foot-long steel span lasted only ten years because the steady increase in railroad loads forced its replacement, but by then steel was coming into general use for all U.S. bridges.

Another legacy of Eads's great arches was their proof that a massive structure did not have to be unsightly. A structure of steel, a material with a strength eight times that of wrought iron, did not need such a profusion of small members, and with increasing knowledge of steel's capacity came more artistic control of its functions. The long-span arch, the most graceful type of bridge, did not come fully into its own until the massive structures of the twentieth century, such as the Hell Gate, linking Long Island with Manhattan. When built in 1916, this soaring arch was both the longest and heaviest bridge of its type in the world. But the cantilever and regular truss forms became extremely popular in the fifty-year spate of steel railroad-bridge construction that preceded the First World War.

The cantilever bridge, consisting of anchored trusses cantilevered out from solid piers and linked by a suspended truss span, appealed to railroad engineers because of its great rigidity and comparative cheapness. In 1876 Charles Shaler Smith threw a cantilevered viaduct over the Kentucky River, and in 1883 Charles C. Schneider carried a railroad track high above the swirling Niagara River on a bridge 910 feet long, with a central cantilever span of 495 feet. Ten years later, the longest railroad cantilever in the United States was built over the Mississippi at Memphis by George S. Morison, an able engineer who combined a 790-foot cantilever span with two 621-foot continuous trusses, one on either side.

The weakness of the continuous truss—a long truss supported at intervals by piers—was the fact that all its members carry stress simultaneously, which necessitates an extremely solid foundation to prevent settlement at any point. A series of hinged trusses, each of which could be accurately assessed as a separate entity, remained the most convenient choice for railroads because they could bridge medium distances speedily and inexpensively with a minimum of calculations and relatively light foundations.

The truss, however, was basically a practical rather than an aesthetic form of support, and it lacked the elegance of the suspension span, with its graceful pattern of suspending cables. The latter had seemed to Eads too flimsy a form to handle the task of carrying both road and rail traffic into a growing city across a great river. Yet the suspension bridge too had undergone a transformation at the hands of a master.

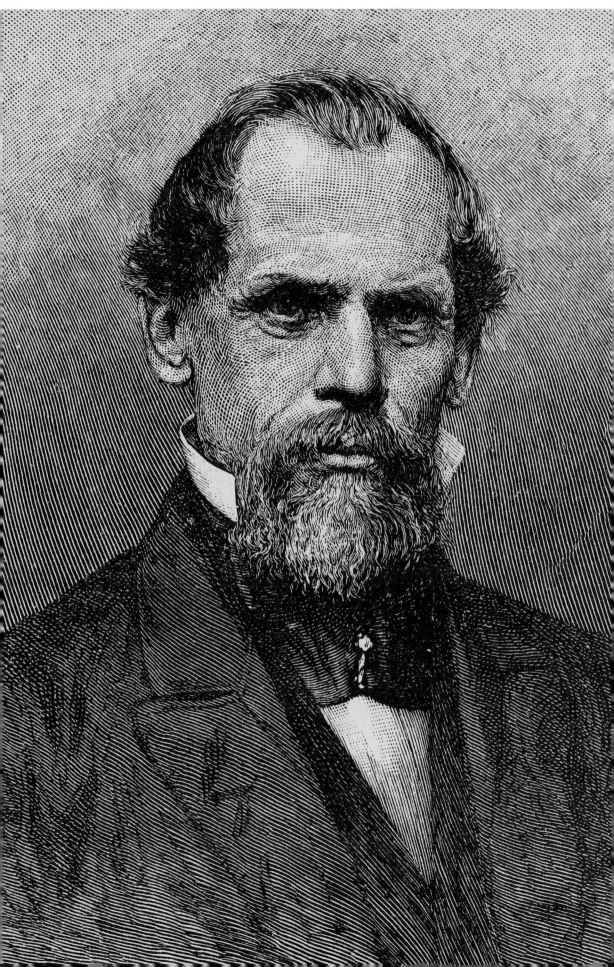

# THE
# SUSPENSION
# SPECTACLE

The modern suspension bridge is an American invention, dating from the beginning of the nineteenth century. But it was in Europe, where the science of engineering was more advanced, that the suspension bridge was analyzed, tested, and perfected. And it was in Europe that the two great builders of American suspension bridges later in the century—Charles Ellet and John Roebling—learned about the subject.

James Finley, a justice of the peace in rural Pennsylvania, invented his suspension bridge in 1801 and built his first example the same year: a short bridge over Jacob's Creek near Uniontown. There had been bridges of the suspension type in ancient China and in scattered places ever since, but generally they were simple affairs with wobbly decks strung from pairs of ropes fastened to both banks of the chasm to be crossed. Finley's design had all the essential characteristics of a modern bridge: two rigid towers; cables slung between the towers in a parabolic curve and anchored into the ground beyond the towers; a stiff and level deck hung from the cables by vertical suspenders.

Finley even published a kind of do-it-yourself manual of suspension-bridge design. Take a board fence, he advised; draw a horizontal line along the bottom—to represent the deck—and mark it off with a series of points. From each of these points draw a perpendicular line upward. Two feet above each of the outermost points drive a nail, and between these nails hang a slackened string, and then attach weighted strings where each of the perpendicular lines intersects the curving string. This de-

fines the curve of the cable and the length of each of the vertical suspenders.

Finley may have recognized that his string, hanging in a curve and bearing weights, approached the correct parabolic curve for equal distribution of weight on a suspension bridge. He may also have known how to position his cable anchors so that the pull on them exactly counterbalanced the pull from the center of the bridge. He probably knew that this was essential if the weight on the towers was to be directly downward. And certainly he recognized that suspension bridges had distinct advantages over truss bridges. They used less material, weighed less, were less expensive, and were potentially the strongest kind of bridge, measured pound for pound. (As an engineer later calculated, a man—with some acrobatic ability—could walk across a gorge one hundred feet wide on a wire weighing only thirteen pounds. A wrought-iron bar capable of carrying a man *plus its own weight* across the same gorge would weigh forty-four tons.)

But it remained for two French engineers, Joseph Cordier and Louis Navier, to put Finley's design on a scientific footing, to analyze the principles of the suspension bridge, and to publish their findings in influential treatises. It cannot be said that they solved all the problems of the new form. Though suspension bridges went up all over Europe, about half of them came tumbling down or were removed out of well-founded fear of collapse. Some of history's worst bridge disasters resulted from the failure of suspension spans between 1830 and 1850.

Into the early and controversial history of the suspension bridge marched Charles Ellet. Born in Pennsylvania in 1810, he might have been a farmer like his Quaker father, had not intellectual curiosity, buttressed by mathematical skills and a superb memory, driven him to more demanding pursuits at the age of seventeen. He worked as surveying assistant on the Chesapeake and Ohio Canal, but saved his pennies and taught himself French so that he could study engineering in Paris. For a year Ellet studied at the Ecole Polytechnique, where the subject of suspension bridges, above all others, excited his imagination. When he returned to America in 1832, he went to Congress with a proposal for a suspension bridge across the Potomac at Washington. Its single span would be a thousand feet long between towers, more than twice as long as any other American suspension bridge. Congress quickly turned down the 22-year-old dreamer. Seven years later, still not having built a single bridge, Ellet proposed to the city of St. Louis to build a 1,200-foot span across the Mississippi for six hundred thousand dollars. The city fathers turned him down, but for the wrong reason: Ellet planned to build his towers on shallow piles, which surely would not have lasted, whereas the city fathers were alarmed at the high cost. (The Eads Bridge was to cost ten times as much.)

In 1841 Ellet at last got a chance to build a bridge to replace Lewis Wernwag's Colossus over the Schuylkill. What he built was not impressive in length, but did employ for the first time in America wrought-iron wire, which was

*showman and an aggressive
salesman of his suspension
bridges. He built only three
of them—in every instance by
underbidding John Roebling,
his great rival. And two of
his bridges collapsed because,
as Roebling realized, they
lacked the necessary stays and
trusses to stiffen the deck.
Ellet should not be judged too
harshly, for some bridge
builders of the 20th century
would make the same mistake.*

far better for cables than the iron chains in use since Finley's time. Five years later Ellet was given a chance to prove he could build a really long suspension span. He was invited to put a highway bridge across the Ohio River at Wheeling. He built it in three years, wrapping sixty-six hundred wires into twelve cables, six to each side of the bridge. With its center span of 1,010 feet, the Wheeling Bridge was the first long-span suspension bridge in the world, and, for a time, the longest single span of any kind.

While working on the Wheeling span, Ellet was invited to bridge the Niagara River, about two miles below the Falls. This was not the sort of commission he could turn down, no matter how busy he was; for although the span would measure only about eight hundred feet, it would cross a high, rugged gorge, at the bottom of which roared the fierce Niagara. Obviously the span, stretching from cliff to cliff almost two hundred and fifty feet above the river, would be a breathtaking thing to see.

As every builder of suspension bridges must do, Ellet had to get a wire across the chasm and over the towers as a beginning step in the placing of cables. With the Wheeling Bridge, this was a simple matter; the first wire was ferried across the river and lifted atop the towers by hoists. But with the rushing Niagara far below in a sharp-angled gorge, ferrying was obviously out of the question. Ellet turned the problem into a memorable public-relations stunt—which was also a practical solution. He offered a prize of five dollars to the first boy to fly a kite across the gorge. A lad named Homan Walsh won the contest amid loud cheers from

a sizable audience that had gathered to watch.

The kite string was used to pull a wire across the chasm, the wire to pull a larger wire, and so on until there stretched across the chasm a cable strong enough to bear the weight of a man. Whereupon Ellet unveiled a special basket he had had made to order. Hooking it to the cable, he hauled himself to the other side and thus became the first man to cross the Niagara gorge. When a rude roadway had been suspended from the cables—it was a narrow service bridge only seven feet wide—Ellet again played the showman. Although the railings were not yet in place, he mounted a horse and rode across—while the sideless span swayed, while the gorge below gaped, while women in the big crowd he had made sure would be on hand screamed and fainted.

With a strengthened deck and the addition of side railings, the service span became a well-used foot and horsemen's bridge. It had cost thirty thousand dollars to build, and in the first year it earned five thousand dollars in tolls. Alongside the service span, Ellet erected a single cable that he used to develop his basket idea. With a four-passenger iron car suspended from the cable, he established a basket ferry across the gorge. At a fare of a dollar a head, it soon paid for itself.

When the directors of the bridge company and Charles Ellet disagreed on the distribution of profits from his side shows, the temperamental designer resigned in 1848 and went back to Wheeling, where, a year later, he completed his bridge across the Ohio.

The bridge was the pride of Wheeling—for a

short while. On May 17, 1854, after just five years of use, it collapsed during a storm. A reporter standing on the riverbank described the death throes: "Lunging like a ship in a storm," the deck "rose to nearly the height of the tower, then fell, and twisted and writhed, and was dashed almost bottom upward." The cables twisted and snapped and the deck crashed into the river. Fortunately, no lives were lost, but the collapse of the Wheeling span put an end to Ellet's career as a bridge builder and he turned his attention to other engineering fields.

The man who, so to speak, picked up the pieces of Ellet's unlucky bridges was John Augustus Roebling, one of the greatest bridge builders of all time. He replaced the Wheeling span and the Niagara span with suspension bridges of his own design, and went on to build others at Pittsburgh and Cincinnati. He designed the greatest span of the nineteenth century, the Brooklyn Bridge, but did not live to see it built. More than a brilliant engineer, Roebling was a man of extraordinary integrity. He envisioned himself a dedicated public servant and he built his bridges as public works.

Born in 1806, Roebling grew up in the Prussian town of Mülhausen; he enrolled in the Royal Polytechnic Institute in Berlin at the age of seventeen, to study architecture and engineering. There he met the noted philosopher Friedrich Hegel, who took a paternal liking to the student. Hegel influenced him in the direction of liberal ideas, including the belief that the United States was a place of destiny. "It is a land of hope for all who are wearied of the historic armory of old Europe," Hegel said.

Roebling was a man for America; certainly he was a misfit for the Prussia of his day. Like most German engineers, he went to work for the government, but his restless, creative mind could not abide the endless rules and restrictions of the German civil service. Moreover, he was a man of liberal ideas in a dreary climate of reactionary politics. In 1831, with a group of like-minded friends, he departed for America.

Together they established a community in western Pennsylvania, naming it Saxonburg, and Roebling became, of necessity, a farmer. But the work could not long hold his interest. In 1837, a year after his marriage and shortly after the birth of his first son, Roebling took a job as a canal surveyor. It was in that capacity that he became familiar with the extraordinary workings of the new Portage Railroad. As he thought about the heavy, rapidly wearing hemp ropes that pulled cars up the inclines, he was struck with an idea: Why not replace the hemp with a rope made of wire? With the help of his Saxonburg neighbors, Roebling put together a wire rope that would prove the worth of his idea. His demonstration on the Portage Railroad failed, but only because a saboteur—paid, probably, by the manufacturer of the hemp rope—had cut through the wire rope. The president of the canal commission was impressed with the product, nevertheless, and ordered it installed on one of the inclines.

Roebling's wire rope began to replace hemp on canal portages everywhere, and the town of Saxonburg now had an industry to support itself. But Roebling was thinking of a more ambitious use of his product. In his last year at the

Royal Polytechnic Institute, he had traveled to Bamberg to see a small suspension bridge being built there. So impressed was he with the bridge that he wrote his graduation thesis on its construction principles.

In 1841 Roebling saw his chance to put his wire to work in a suspension bridge. He signed on as an assistant to the contractor who was to build a bridge across the Schuylkill to replace Wernwag's Colossus. At the last minute the contract was rescinded—and awarded instead to Charles Ellet. Thus began their rivalry.

Three years later, when an aqueduct carrying a canal over the Allegheny River in Pittsburgh was destroyed by ice, Roebling at last gained his opportunity. Responding to an offer of a hundred-dollar prize for the best plan to replace the old structure, he presented a model of a suspension span. The judges were skeptical about the ability of a slender cable to support a heavy wooden trough filled with water, but they were impressed with the speed and economy with which it could be built, and so gave Roebling the job. Unlike Ellet, who used the French system of constructing the cable on the ground before hoisting it into place, Roebling used a system that made better sense; each wire of the cable was put into position on the bridge, one after another, until the cable had been built up in the exact position it would occupy on the completed structure. Thus the curve was built into the cable from the beginning, not forced on a cable that had been laid straight. Roebling also insulated his cables with tightly wrapped iron wire.

During the construction of the aqueduct, a disastrous fire in Pittsburgh destroyed an old bridge across the Monongahela and Roebling promptly proposed to replace it with a suspension bridge for the attractively low price of fifty-five thousand dollars. His offer was accepted, and he went to work on a bridge fifteen hundred feet long, consisting of eight suspension spans. When the Monongahela Bridge was finished in 1846, Roebling turned to building more aqueducts, this time for the Delaware and Hudson Canal. By mid-century he had built six suspension spans, five of them as aqueducts, and was well established as the world's leading builder of suspension bridges.

So it was that when Ellet quit the Niagara project, Roebling was called in. He was still building that bridge when, in 1854, news of the collapse of Ellet's Wheeling Bridge rekindled the fears, already widespread, that Roebling was attempting the impossible. So Roebling quickly issued a report on the faults of the Wheeling Bridge and the superiority of his building techniques. "The destruction of the Wheeling Bridge," he wrote, "was clearly owing to a want of stability, and not to a want of strength. This want of stiffness could have been supplied by *over-floor stays*, *truss railings*, *under-floor stays*, or *cable stays*." The Niagara Bridge, he pointed out, would be stabilized by most of these features. Since there would be two decks, one for a railroad, the other for a highway, the superstructure would be in the form of a rigid, hollow box, built of strong girders and trusses. Radiating from the towers down to the decks would be sixty-four stabilizing wire ropes, called stays. And just to be

Stricken by caisson disease,
Washington Roebling sat at a
window in his Brooklyn Heights
home to watch progress on
his bridge and, with pained
fingers, to write memoranda to
his engineering assistants.
His devoted wife, Emily (right),
taught herself engineering
and acted as his secretary and
emissary. In the picture
below, the artist has added
the violin as a melodramatic
touch; Roebling, of course, was
no longer able to play it.

sure, Roebling was putting fifty-six stays under the bridge, anchored in the solid rock of the cliffs. In a report filed after the bridge had been completed in 1855, Roebling reiterated the secret of his success: "The means employed are *Weight, Girders, Trusses,* and *Stays.*" The Niagara Bridge held up.

Roebling rebuilt the Wheeling span, completed a bridge across the Allegheny in Pittsburgh, and in 1856 began a 1,200-foot span across the Ohio at Cincinnati. His son Washington, who had studied bridge engineering at Rensselaer Polytechnic Institute, joined him as assistant on the latter projects—in the case of Cincinnati, not until the close of the Civil War and the completion of a dashing career as a Union officer. They worked well together and shared pride and credit when the Cincinnati Bridge, then the biggest of the world's bridges, was opened late in 1866. It had taken ten years—marked by accidents and floods, financial setbacks and rising prices, and the exigencies of war—to complete. It had taxed John Roebling's spirit, and as he approached his sixtieth birthday, he confessed he was ready to "leave bridge-building to younger folks."

But not quite yet. In 1857 Roebling had proposed building a bridge sixteen hundred feet long across the East River, linking the cities of Brooklyn and New York. Earlier proposals had been rejected because the bridge appeared an engineering impossibility or would cost too much; because Brooklyn and New York were independent and rival cities; because the ferryboat owners openly opposed it. Nothing came of Roebling's proposal until 1865, when a few

Brooklyn citizens and a few New York legislators backed the plan. The harsh winter of 1866–67, when ice choked the river and ferries were stranded, convinced many others and in April the necessary legislation was passed. Still there were doubters; the bridge would be 50 per cent longer than the Cincinnati span, and, with its tramways and vehicle paths and walkways, would bear a weight of 18,700 tons. It cannot be built, its detractors said; even if it could, it would never pay off. But Roebling submitted every detail to a board of engineering consultants, and in the spring of 1869 they pronounced his plan "entirely practicable."

On July 6 of that year, John Roebling stood on a cluster of piles at a ferry slip, calculating the precise location for the Brooklyn tower. While he was absorbed in his figuring, a docking ferryboat smashed against the fender of the slip. The impact forced the fender back against the piles, and Roebling's foot, wedged between some of the timbers, was crushed.

The toes on his right foot had to be amputated, but even then tetanus set in. For two weeks Roebling lived with excruciating pain. On July 21, resigning himself to a long convalescence, he designed an elaborate apparatus to lift and lower him in bed and ordered it built at once. The next morning John Roebling was dead.

In August the directors appointed 32-year-old Washington Roebling to the position of chief engineer of the Brooklyn Bridge.

He was in many ways his father's son: dedicated democrat, tenacious researcher, gifted engineer. But in many ways he was his own man. John Roebling had been a German-

American, liberal by conviction, but earnest, orderly, disciplined in his personal affairs. Washington Roebling, American-born, was impulsive, pragmatic, not so much the planner as his father, but probably a better improviser. If there were doubts about Washington Roebling being the match of his father, they were in time dispelled.

For the foundation of the Brooklyn tower, Roebling had a massive caisson built, in which timber walls of the working chamber were tapered at bottom and sheathed with iron to provide a cutting edge. At the place where the caisson was to be sunk, Roebling first of all had thousands of cubic feet of mud removed by blasting and dredging; to keep the rectangular hole from filling up again, he walled it on three sides with timber pilings. By May of 1870 the caisson was in place, and workmen descended to the air chamber to begin the digging.

The work went slowly. The clay was sometimes so compact that it had to be pried loose with steel bars. Huge boulders had to be wrenched out of the way before they mashed the iron cutting edge. The largest of these had to be split into pieces before they could be hauled up through the water shaft. When the caisson was twenty-five feet below water level, the boulders were so huge that removal of them called for blasting—something that had never been tried in the pressurized atmosphere of a caisson. Characteristically, Washington Roebling personally conducted the experiments that proved blasting safe. After that, the average progress in sinking the caisson went from six inches a week to twice that.

There were anxious moments. Occasionally the air pressure in the chamber would overbalance the pressure of the water it was holding out, a huge bubble would escape under the edge, and water would come rushing in. The biggest such "blowout" occurred, fortunately, on a Sunday when no workmen were in the chamber. A watchman had forgotten to seal the water shaft, and when the pressure in the working chamber rose to a certain point, the contents of the shaft reacted like a pent-up cork in a champagne bottle. With a deafening roar, mud and water shot five hundred feet into the air, raining down on buildings on the Brooklyn water front.

When the caisson reached deep into the river bed, the threat of blowouts and floods diminished, but the increased air pressure made another threat all the more hazardous: fire. It struck on December 2, 1870. Calking caught fire, and the air pressure drove the flames up into the roof timbers. Efforts to smother the fire with carbon dioxide and to drown it with hosed water proved futile, and the next day Roebling called upon fireboats to flood the whole caisson. That stopped the fire but did not undo the damage. After the caisson was pumped dry, thin cement grout was forced upward through holes to fill spaces burned away. The grouting was premature; investigation showed that, deep inside, roof timbers were charred. The grout had to be removed, the timbers scraped down to solid wood, and the cavities once again filled with grout.

While the caisson was going down, the masonry work on top was rising, and in June,

# Brooklyn Daily Eagle

FRIDAY EVENING, JUNE 14, 1878.

# THE BRIDGE.

## A Somewhat Sensational Incident To-day.

## A CRASH.

## Fatal and Startling Accident on the Bridge To-day.

**A Partially Constructed Cable Slips at the New York End and is Precipitated Into the River—Water Splashed Fifty Feet Into the Air— Narrow Escape of the Ferryboat Farragut— One Man Killed Outright, Another Fatally Injured and Three Others Hurt—The Matter Thoroughly Inquired Into—How it All Came to Pass—A Point not Clear—Was Bessemer Steel to Blame ?**

About 12 o'clock to-day the people along the line of the Bridge upon the New York side were startled by a loud report, closely followed by a furious rushing sound, as if a tornado had struck the city. It was a strand of the No. 4 cable of the Bridge which had been released in some manner (described fully below) from the New York anchorage, and by the weight of its centre was drawn with frightful rapidity through the air.

The accident is the first of its kind that has yet occurred, and it has a sad result, since by it one man was killed outright and another is likely to die, while three others were more or less injured.

The strand, composed of about 400 wires, was firmly attached upon the Brooklyn anchorage, and was bound as far as the New York pier. Released, as it was, from the New York side, it slid through the grooves of the New York pier and fell into the river with all the force the weight of forty-nine tons could give it, while the water shot up in the air to the height of fifty feet, stretching across the river like a huge wall suddenly raised up.

In its descent it narrowly escaped striking one of the Union Ferry boats, the Farragut, which was crossing on the Fulton Ferry from New York to the Brooklyn side. As it was the boat was damaged by the water. Had this strand with its enormous weight struck the ferryboat a longer list of dead and wounded would have been printed in the EAGLE of to-night.

The general impression seems to be that the strand parted, but such is not the case. It was the rope of the fall, by which the strand is lowered into place and attached to the shoe around which the wire of the strand is passed, which parted.

This wire rope was the only thing which held back

1875, the Brooklyn tower reached its height of 316 feet. In the meantime, work had begun on the foundation of the New York tower, where the caisson had to be sunk deeper and support a greater weight of masonry. Roebling had one built with a roof twenty-two feet thick, incorporating features designed to prevent the setbacks that had occurred in the Brooklyn caisson. Digging went rapidly and without incident—until the caisson approached its final depth of eighty feet below water level and the pressure in the chamber rose to thirty-six pounds. Then the dreaded caisson disease—which had plagued work on the Eads Bridge two years earlier—came to the Brooklyn Bridge. In the first five months of 1872, 110 cases required medical treatment and three workmen died. And then one day the disease struck the man who had spent so much time in the caisson, close to his workmen, supervising the digging.

Crippled, nearly voiceless, in constant pain, Washington Roebling was maimed for life. Nobody, however, replaced him. From his sickroom in Brooklyn Heights he could see the bridge. Using binoculars to observe progress, he continued to direct all operations, his wife serving as his voice and messenger.

The towers were thus completed and the anchorages built on both shores of the river. The spinning of the cables began in 1876. The Brooklyn Bridge was to be the first suspension bridge to use steel instead of iron, and steel was still a novel material for American manufacturers. As James Eads had done, Roebling insisted that every piece of steel wire be thoroughly tested before use. But the contractor who supplied the wire began a colossal swindle. After a wagonload of wire passed inspection, the contractor's teamsters, instead of hauling the wire to the bridge, unloaded it, substituted inferior wire, and hid the good wire, which they later picked up to run through the same cycle of deception. By the time the sleight of hand was discovered, an incalculable amount of inferior wire had been spun into the cable. Roebling could not dismantle his bridge; instead he required the contractor to supply enough extra wire of acceptable strength to make up for the deficiency.

Back and forth from anchor to anchor, across the great towers and in a gentle curve between them, the wires were laid. Groups of them were bound together to form a strand, and then nineteen strands were gathered and compressed into cylindrical shape to form each of the four great cables. Then the suspenders were hung from iron sleeves around the cables, and the crossbeams—lattice girders, built of steel—were attached to the suspenders. By the end of 1881, all that remained was the laying of the decks on top of the crossbeams.

And all the while the Brooklyn Bridge remained the center of a public storm. In 1875, when capital had run out and rumors were abroad that the directors of the bridge company had pocketed some of it, the project was turned over to the cities of Brooklyn and New York. Three years later, Roebling announced that he had used up the thirteen and a half million dollars authorized for the bridge, which already was far more than the seven million dol-

lars his father had estimated for the job ten years earlier. All of the old arguments were hauled out to support the clamor, once again, to bring the project to a halt. For six months work did in fact halt, until new funds were authorized. Then, in 1881, Roebling pressed his declining luck by asking for an additional one thousand tons of steel because he had changed the deck design to strengthen it. Public furor swelled, fed by innuendo about Roebling's mental health. There was a move to have him fired. But eventually Roebling won out, and by his persistence gave the Brooklyn Bridge the strength it would need for the loads it was destined to carry.

On May 24, 1883, Washington Roebling sat at his window and focused his binoculars on the bridge. No debris littered its approaches, no wires hung loose, no workmen teetered on the cables. The gray granite towers stood tall, strong, and majestic, and the cables and suspenders and stays shimmered in the sun. The mayors of New York and Brooklyn were at the bridge; so were Governor Grover Cleveland and President Chester Arthur; and so were thousands of spectators.

John Roebling, two decades earlier, had promised that the Brooklyn Bridge "will not only be the greatest bridge in existence, but it will be the greatest engineering work of this continent, and of the age." The statement had a kind of Prussian arrogance, but it was not exaggerated. Admired by generations of architects and engineers, celebrated by poets and painters, the Brooklyn Bridge has been all that Roebling claimed for it.

# PORTFOLIO:
# THE BROOKLYN BRIDGE

T*he first man to cross over New York's East River by way of the Brooklyn Bridge was a modest, middle-aged engineer named E. F. Farrington. Seated in a tiny bosun's chair, he soared from Brooklyn to New York and back again slung from a 3/4-inch wire rope that stretched from shore to shore and over the bridge's recently completed stone towers. Farrington made his trip on an August afternoon in 1876, with cannon booming and huge crowds roaring their approval all the way. For everyone on both sides of the water, it appeared that at long last the most celebrated engineering dream of the age was actually going to come true. Six years of intensive work had already gone into the bridge, and there would be seven more before it was finished. Several of the important details of that project are depicted in the special portfolio that follows.*

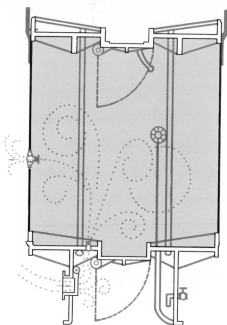

**THE BRIDGE BEGAN** *with the foundations for two gigantic granite towers, each of which would weigh 80,000 tons and would have to rest firm and true deep in the river bed. The problem was solved with caissons, immense bottomless boxes built of solid timber about 20 feet thick on top and with sides 8 feet thick tapering to an iron-sheathed cutting edge about 8 inches thick. Inside, where the men would work, the whole affair was calked tight as a ship and lined with iron boiler plate. As layer on layer of stone blocks were built on top, the floating box sank until it hit bottom. Then compressed air was used to force the water out of the work area and crews of sand hogs (as they were called) went down to dig.*

*To keep the compressed air from escaping, the well-like entrances had air locks (diagram at left). As the men descended, they would enter the top of the air lock through a hatch, close it, then release a valve at the base of the lock to admit compressed air from below. When the air pressure inside the lock equaled that of the work area (pictured in the small engraving, far left), the bottom hatch was opened and the men climbed down out of the air lock. Before the next group came down, the compressed air would be released from the lock through a side valve, and thus the only compressed air lost was that which had been released from the lock.*

*To have hauled out mud and rock the same way would have been far too tedious, so clam buckets were used, working from above in water locks. (The water in these locks had to be maintained at a level sufficient to prevent the compressed air from blowing out from below.) The men kept the buckets supplied by shoveling mud and rock into pits at the base of each water lock. As they dug deeper and deeper and as the tower continued to grow overhead, the caisson sank until it found solid footing. Then the caisson's work area and shafts were filled with concrete and permanently sealed off below.*

**THE COMPLETED TOWERS** *stood 276 feet above the river level, making them far and away the tallest structures on the New York sky line, except for the steeple on Trinity Church. The engraving gives some indication of the view from the top of the completed Brooklyn tower. (The half-finished New York tower and Lower Manhattan's then modest sky line are seen in the distance.) From the center of one tower to the other—the dotted line in the diagram—was 1595.50 feet. The blue line indicates the span of a temporary footbridge, which was slung from tower to tower not long after E. F. Farrington took his pioneering ride. The yellow line marks the arc of a storm rope used to steady the footbridge, while the great curve of the cables from which the steel bridge deck would hang is shown in purple. The profile of the deck itself is drawn in red. The width of the deck was to be 85 feet and its altitude above the water, 135 feet, would provide ample clearance for most river traffic of the time—except for some of the biggest of the sailing ships, such as the* Great Republic, *which is represented at far right in the diagram.*

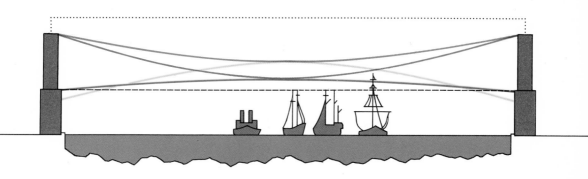

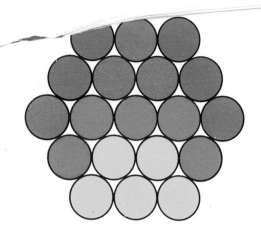

**TO CONNECT THE TOWERS** *a wire rope was hoisted over the Brooklyn tower, one end secured on shore, the other ferried across to the New York tower, where it was hoisted over the top and then wound up on a winch until clear of the river. A second wire was strung in the same way; the two were joined to make an endless belt or "traveler" rope reaching across from anchorage to anchorage. That done, the four cables could be spun in air. Individual wires were carried across by a wheel fixed to the traveler rope. The wires were laid in "strands" of 278 wires and 19 strands formed a cable 15.75 inches in diameter. (The diagram shows the order in which the strands were built up: yellow was the first tier, blue the second, red the third, purple the fourth.) Then the cables were compacted into circular form, clamped, and wrapped with a layer of iron wire (as shown below).*

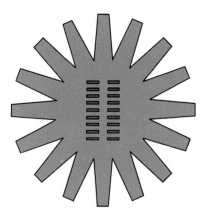

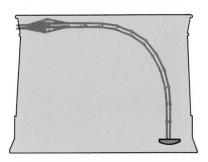

**THE VAST WEIGHT** *of the deck was carried by the four completed cables, which were fixed to two massive masonry anchorages on the opposite shores. At the top of the anchorages each cable was attached to chains of iron anchor bars (indicated in red in the diagrams and pictured in the foreground below). The chains were in turn attached to big iron anchor plates, called "mushrooms" (shown in blue), which were imbedded at the base of each anchorage. Then to the cables, iron suspender bands were attached, and to these were fixed wire rope suspenders (right), which would hold the steel floor beams of the deck. With the suspenders in place, the first crossbeams of the deck could be hung, beginning with those closest to the anchorages and towers. The nearest suspenders had only to be drawn in, the beam attached and swung out into place, ready to support planks for the workmen to stand on as they launched the second beam, and so on until the decks, proceeding out over the river from both towers, met at the center.*

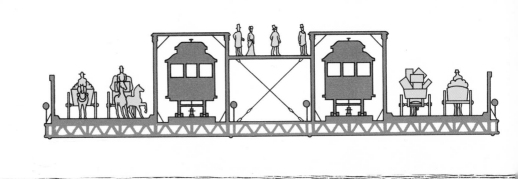

**EN THE BRIDGE WAS FINISHED** *in May of 1883, two cities had been made into one metropolis of nearly two million people. In terms of popular appeal, few structures ever built in America can compare to the Brooklyn Bridge; as a piece of engineering it was and remains one of the world's great achievements. The center span was 1595.50 feet long and the two end spans were each 930 feet. It would be almost 50 years before a significantly longer span would be built, and so sound was the bridge's structural integrity that it would be nearly 70 years before major reinforcements would be needed. The diagram at left shows how the design laid out by the Roeblings separated carriage, rail, and pedestrian traffic. The fare on the bridge's rail cars was five cents and the ride took about five minutes. But as one writer of the day pointed out, "The wise man will not cross the bridge in five minutes, nor in twenty. He will linger to get the good of the splendid sweep of view about him, which his aesthetic self will admit pays wonderful interest on his investment of nothing."*

# A GREAT
# TIME FOR
# DOING

The difficult we do immediately," goes the old Army slogan; "the impossible takes a little longer." And the claim is a fair summary of the spirit that infected the American people as they altered the face of the continent to serve their ends. The spirit was there when Clinton dug his ditch; when the Hoosac engineers dug their tunnel, when Eads spanned the Mississippi, when the Roeblings built the Brooklyn Bridge.

The spirit of obstacles-be-damned was there again as the United States undertook, in 1904, to dig the Panama Canal. The idea of a man-made water route through Central America to link the oceans was an old one: Spanish explorers had talked of it early in the sixteenth century, and Portuguese, German, French, English, and American dreamers and schemers had been proposing a canal at intervals ever since. In 1827, the aging German poet, Johann Wolfgang von Goethe, foresaw that America would construct the canal. He knew that the United States, in time, would expand to the Pacific Coast. "It is absolutely indispensable," he told a friend, "for the United States to effect a passage from the Mexican Gulf to the Pacific Ocean; and I am certain that they will do it. Would that I might live to see it!"

The French almost proved Goethe wrong. In 1879, Ferdinand de Lesseps, who a decade earlier had built the great Suez Canal in Egypt, helped to organize a private company in France to dig a canal across the Isthmus of Panama. De Lesseps was no engineer but a beguiling promoter, and when he said that a sea-level canal—one with no locks at all—

*One of the Panama Canal's giant steel lock gates gets a fresh coat of paint.*

could be built, it did not matter that eminent engineers disagreed. One hundred thousand Frenchmen, most of them small investors, rushed to buy stock in the enterprise.

The canal would be less than half as long as the 103-mile Suez. But the terrain would reach to a height of 330 feet, whereas the maximum for the Suez Canal had been 50. Moreover, the terrain was rocky, not sandy, though in places the rock was destined to behave like sand by sliding down the slopes of excavations. And lastly, in place of the dry heat of Egypt lay the tropical heat of Panama—hard on machines, debilitating to men, nourishing to the insects that bore yellow fever and malaria.

De Lesseps began digging in 1881, and, in each succeeding year, issued optimistic reports on the progress. In 1887 he finally had to admit that locks would be necessary (though he deemed them only temporary), and he commissioned Gustave Eiffel, builder of the famous Paris tower, to construct the lock gates. Eiffel never built them. On December 14, 1888, France awoke to the shocking news that De Lesseps' company was bankrupt and had been assigned to receivers. During the next few years, France and the world learned why. De Lesseps' company had hired contractors under incredibly liberal terms, had allowed money to be siphoned off for work never done, had paid New York bankers fat salaries for promoting American investment in the canal (which the bankers never did), had paid French newspapers for favorable publicity, had bribed politicians to give support to the project. In 1893, Ferdinand de Lesseps, his son Charles, and

several others were criminally convicted and consigned to ignominy. A new company was formed to keep the canal project going, but it ran out of capital, and in 1898 offered to sell the partly finished canal to the United States.

All the while the French company was digging its Panama waterway, the United States was considering a canal of its own through Nicaragua. Though the route would be longer, it would be closer to home, and thus would save time in coast-to-coast shipping. But the idea never rallied enough support to get congressional approval. Among the active opponents of the Nicaraguan canal was James Eads, whose proposal for an alternative was a "ship railway" across southern Mexico. Under Eads's scheme, ships would be floated onto a cradle and hauled across the 134-mile distance on twelve pairs of rails by huge locomotives.

Eads's proposal died, but the Nicaraguan canal idea lived on, even after the United States had agreed on terms for the purchase of the French canal in Panama. A treaty had to be negotiated with Colombia, of which Panama was then a province, and President Theodore Roosevelt grew impatient with the dallying of Colombia officials over the draft he had presented them. Then, in one of the less honorable episodes of American diplomatic history, the United States connived to support the secession of Panama; an American gunboat was sitting in Colón harbor on the day the Panama junta announced secession. With impolitic speed the United States recognized the independence of Panama and just as quickly concluded a canal treaty with the new country.

It was all too indelicate for some of Roosevelt's countrymen, but the President had a message for his critics: "Tell them that I am going to make the dirt fly on the Isthmus." The United States paid the French company four million dollars for the unfinished canal and its construction machinery. Almost as soon as the French engineers handed over the keys to their warehouses and the rotting equipment they contained, the dirt indeed began to fly. Digging was begun to satisfy the public eagerness for signs of progress, even though there was not yet a new plan for the canal, even though the crucial issue of sea-level versus lock canal had not yet been settled.

The hasty digging was Roosevelt's first mistake; his second was to place canal affairs in the hands of a seven-man commission of engineering experts. The commissioners, meeting two thousand miles away from the canal site, bickering with one another, caused delays in the work and confusion among the engineers actually on the job. Overreacting to the French experience of extravagant outlays for equipment, the commissioners introduced penny-pinching procedures and red tape that further hampered the work. In June, 1905, John Findley Wallace, chief resident engineer, resigned in disgust. His successor, John F. Stevens, was a distinguished railroad engineer who successfully made the transition to canal-building. Though he had a new and more liberal commission with which to work, Stevens also was the target of criticism and interference, and he lasted only until April, 1907.

By now, Roosevelt was disgusted too. Determined to put the work "in charge of men who will stay on the job until I get tired of having them there," he turned the project over to the U.S. Army. To head the project he needed a man of strong will and executive ability, able to cope with red tape, able to handle the virtually unlimited power Roosevelt was about to give him. Roosevelt found his tsar in Lieutenant Colonel George Washington Goethals, a 49-year-old West Pointer who had been chief of Army engineers during the Spanish-American War.

The announcement of a change in command sent a shock wave across the isthmus. Workmen feared they would lose their jobs to regiments of infantrymen, or that their lives at the canal would be made miserable by bugles and salutes and inspections. When Goethals arrived, he sought to allay their fears. "There will be no more militarism in the future than there has been in the past," he said. For the most part, he fulfilled the promise. But Goethals himself was a thorough militarist: stern and abrupt, accustomed to giving orders and having them obeyed. "You are not very far along," he said to a foreman one day.

"I know, Colonel. But we are doing our best."

"I don't expect you to do your best," Goethals snapped. "I expect you to complete your work on time."

Goethals shamed and frightened the men to greater output, but he also had another military device for serving the same end: competition. He started a weekly canal newspaper in which he published statistics on the output

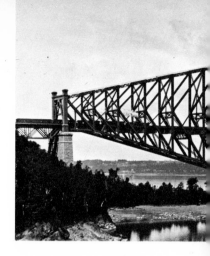

of each working crew and the costs of the work done. That spurred the necessary rivalry among crews, but just to make sure, Goethals also introduced intramural baseball.

Under Stevens' administration, the route of the canal had been determined, and, for the most part, Goethals had only to get it dug. From the breakwaters jutting into the Caribbean, the canal was to be dug southward (not from east to west, as we tend to imagine) at sea level for a short distance. Then a series of three locks would carry ships a vertical distance of eighty-five feet into a man-made lake twenty-three miles long. At the far end of the lake there would be a nine-mile cut through the Panama hills, then another lock, a small artificial lake, and two more locks to carry ships down to the level of the Pacific, a few miles away.

One hundred million cubic yards of material had to be removed from the Culebra Cut through the Panama hills, thirty million cubic yards as a result of repeated landslides. Six thousand men were put to work in the cut, drilling and blasting away at the hillside, operating the steam shovels that clawed at the debris, running trainloads of rock and dirt to dump sites. Everything was on a colossal scale: 95-ton shovels picked up eight tons of material at a scoop; 140 locomotives, pulling 3,700 flatcars, plied back and forth over 130 miles of track more than a million times a year. Sixty million tons of dynamite were set off. Culebra cost ten million dollars a mile.

Under Goethals' prodding, the dirt flew faster and faster. The 1907 record of one million cubic yards of excavation a month—almost enough to fill the Empire State Building—was soon doubled, and when a monthly record of three million cubic yards was reached, Goethals determined that the new record should become the average. He got his way.

Thirty million tons of material had to go into the earth dam to hold back the Chagres River and create Gatun Lake. Here again was a project on a gargantuan scale: a dam 105 feet high and a mile and a half long, half a mile wide at the base. When the dam was finished in 1913, the waters rose behind it, filling a lake 164 square miles in area, then the world's largest man-made body of water.

And then there were the massive locks: each 1,000 feet long and 110 wide, arranged side-by-side in pairs for two-way traffic, separated by a wall 60 feet wide, resting on a concrete floor 13 feet thick. The steel lock gates were 7 feet thick and the smallest of them were 47 feet high and weighed 390 tons; others were nearly twice as big and heavy.

Lastly, there were the men—at the peak of activity, fifty-six thousand of them toiling in the tropical heat. The U.S. government fed and housed them, dispensing comforts in degrees according to rank and pay. The Americans were at the top of the caste society in the Canal Zone, above the European laborers, far above the West Indian Negroes. "The Brahmin caste itself," a resident noted, "is divided and subdivided into infinitesimal gradations. Every rank and shade of man has a different salary, and exactly in accordance with that salary is he housed, furnished, and treated down to the

last item—number of electric lights, candle power, style of bed, size of bookcase." One government expenditure that was universally appreciated was the four million dollars spent on sanitation—especially for the program, under Colonel William C. Gorgas, to eradicate yellow fever and malaria.

The Panama Canal was appropriately acclaimed "the greatest engineering feat of the ages," but it was completed in 1914 with an astonishing lack of fanfare. Perhaps American minds were preoccupied with the war then raging in Europe. Perhaps their confidence in the American ability to conquer obstacles made the achievement less meaningful. Perhaps, because the canal was so far from home, they really could not appreciate the magnitude of the achievement. And once the machines of construction had been dismantled and the armies of workers had returned home, as soon as the waters poured in over much of what they had accomplished, the moment for full appreciation of the Panama Canal had passed.

In truth, America's confidence in its engineering prowess was not without an undercurrent of apprehension. The building of the Panama Canal had been attended by frequent rumors that the engineers were bungling. Their plans for the earth dam to create Gatun Lake recalled memories of the Johnstown flood of 1889, when an earth dam collapsed and sent millions of tons of water through the Conemaugh Valley of Pennsylvania, wreaking destruction and killing two thousand people. There were those who were sure the Gatun Dam would not hold, especially when they read newspaper reports of its rock heaps settling into soft ground underneath as the dam was being built. But the engineers knew that the rocks would settle, knew that they were building a dam sufficiently strong and impervious. The dam held.

Similarly, bridge-building early in the twentieth century was attended by memories of the Ashtabula disaster of 1876 and the equally tragic collapse three years later of the Firth of Tay Bridge in Scotland. Against the lingering apprehensions stood the unmistakably great accomplishments of Eads and the Roeblings, and the reassuring fact that steel was replacing iron as the basic material for bridges. Then, late in August of 1907, came the jolting news of the worst bridge-building disaster in history. The incident blemished the American record, for, while the bridge was in Canada, its designer was Theodore Cooper, then one of the foremost of American bridge engineers.

The bridge over the St. Lawrence at Quebec was to be eighteen hundred feet long, setting a record for steel cantilever bridges. It was nearly finished when a bottom chord member suddenly crumpled and twenty thousand tons of steelwork crashed to the river, carrying seventy-five workmen to their deaths. Earlier, word had been sent to Cooper in his New York office that one of the cantilevered spans had deflected downward a fraction of an inch, and Cooper had ordered an investigation. When he learned that work on the bridge was proceeding as usual, he ordered it stopped immediately. But his telegram arrived too late.

The collapse of the Quebec Bridge finished

"It is rather odd," wrote novelist Theodore Dreiser in August of 1915, "to stand in the presence of so great a thing in the making and realize that you are looking at one of the true wonders of the world." Like so many other sightseers who showed up in northeastern Pennsylvania between 1912 and 1915, Dreiser had only superlatives to describe the Tunkhannock Viaduct, an immense concrete bridge then being built near Scranton. The bridge was the centerpiece for a 39-mile, $12-million cutoff on the Lackawanna Railroad that included monstrous embankments, numerous cuts, a tunnel, and two other viaducts. No concrete bridge of such size had

ever been attempted before, and everyone who
turned out to watch was treated to a splendid
show. Across an aerial cableway strung from
one end of the valley to the other, big
buckets of concrete soared overhead, poised
momentarily, then dumped their contents into
huge timber forms. Hundreds of men were at
work, along with steam shovels by the dozen,
steam hoists, concrete mixers, and locomotives.
None of the crew was buried alive in the
wet concrete, as legend would have it, but two
died in falls. The scale of the finished
bridge (which was 2,375 feet long, 240 feet
high) was made vividly clear when the first
trains started across (bottom photograph).

Cooper's career. And, like the Ashtabula disaster three decades earlier, it made civil engineers take a new and harder look at their calculations and their standards. During the next ten years the Quebec Bridge was rebuilt along sounder lines; it was the scene of another tragic accident in 1916, when the 5,200-ton center span fell as it was being hoisted into place and killed eleven workmen. The following year the operation was performed with greater care and the bridge completed.

Apprehension and occasional failure also accompanied the introduction of a new material for the twentieth century: reinforced concrete. As engineers learned more about concrete and ways of strengthening it with iron and steel rods, they began using it with confidence and for increasingly ambitious projects. U.S. production of Portland cement, the basic ingredient of concrete, rose from eight million barrels in 1900 to seventy-six million in 1910, to more than double that in 1925. (Five million cubic yards of concrete went into the building of the Panama Canal, which became a proving ground for better mechanical means of mixing and handling the material.) The first American concrete bridge had been built in Prospect Park in Brooklyn in 1871, and the first reinforced one in Golden Gate Park in San Francisco in 1889. Both were timid beginnings, having spans of only twenty feet. But by the turn of the century, reinforced concrete arches more than one hundred feet long were being used in bridges.

Concrete won the favor of railroad builders; the famous Florida East Coast Railroad route across the Florida Keys, completed in 1912, had a total of nearly six miles of concrete spans. In 1915, the Delaware, Lackawanna, and Western Railroad completed the longest reinforced concrete arch bridge in the world: the Tunkhannock Viaduct north of Scranton, Pennsylvania. It was 2,375 feet long, and its ten graceful arches supported a deck 240 feet above Tunkhannock Valley.

Concrete and steel were transforming American cities, crowding them with ever taller buildings, and as civil engineering entered the twentieth century, it was perfecting a technique vital to some of the largest cities: soft-ground tunneling. New York needed it most of all; it needed subways to relieve the congestion on its streets, and it needed tunnels under its rivers to link Manhattan with Brooklyn and Manhattan with New Jersey. In the latter case, bridges were no substitute; even if the broad Hudson could be spanned, a bridge would have to be high enough to let ships pass beneath, and that would put it too high for the railroads. To get trains to that level would require very long approaches and hence too much valuable Manhattan acreage.

Most of the nineteenth-century advances in soft-ground tunneling were made abroad, especially in London, where problems similar to New York's were faced earlier and solved sooner. Soft-ground tunneling required techniques different from those of hard-rock tunneling, since the basic difficulty is not removing material but preventing its collapse into the excavation. Under rivers especially, water as well as earth has to be held back.

Giant tunnels also became the order of the day in the 20th century. The new automobile tunnel under the Hudson River, between Manhattan and New Jersey, was the longest underwater vehicular tunnel and the first to use tremendous fans for ventilation. The designer was a young engineer, Clifford Holland (left), who died of overwork before the tunnel was finished in 1927; it was named for him. Three vehicles of the era (below) pass through in 1935.

In London in 1825, an expatriate French engineer named Marc Brunel began to dig a tunnel under the Thames River. It took him eighteen years, through repeated floodings and other mishaps, and it cost three million dollars. Brunel's troubles discouraged anyone from attempting another subaqueous tunnel for a quarter-century, but the experience proved the worth of his great invention, the tunneling shield. This was a device, built to the size of the tunnel's cross section, for controlling the material at the working face. It facilitated digging but prevented great slides of soft material into the tunnel. Brunel's was built up of twelve narrow frames, side by side, each twenty-two feet high and containing platforms for three workmen, one above another. Together the cast-iron frames weighed eighty tons and composed a rectangle thirty-eight feet wide. Wooden boards connected by extendible rods to the frames held back the material at the working face; before digging, the boards were removed, one at a time, and then replaced in a new, forward position. Masons built the brick lining of the tunnel behind the shield, and when it came time to move the whole shield forward, the workmen turned jackscrews that pushed against the lining.

A second tunnel under the Thames was begun in 1869, this time with a vastly improved shield and with the able direction of James H. Greathead, a 25-year-old South African engineer. Greathead got the tunnel dug in less than a year, for the sum of one hundred thousand dollars. At the same time, Alfred Ely Beach, editor of *Scientific American* and an accom-

plished inventor, was digging a tunnel under Broadway in New York, using a shield of his own design. Beach's tunnel was only the length of a football field, but it was New York's first subway and a brilliant demonstration of an idea that is still very much alive: a cylindrical rail car propelled through a closely fitting tube. Beach wanted to extend the project to provide New York a rapid-transit system, but politicians connived against it and investors spurned him, and in 1873 he sealed the tunnel in disgust.

Greathead and others, observing the success of the pneumatic caisson in bridge-building, came to recognize the value of its principle for tunnel-digging. Seeping water was a frequent hazard in soft-ground tunneling; by increasing the air pressure in a tunnel, they would be able to hold the water back. In 1873 a wealthy Californian, De Witt Clinton Haskin, undertook the digging of a railroad tunnel under the Hudson, using the compressed-air method. Haskin's mistake was not using a shield as well. There was far greater water pressure at the bottom of the 22-foot-high working face than at the top, and a pressure sufficient to hold all the water would have been too great at the top—resulting in air leakage up through the silt and the decided risk of a major blowout. The solution was a compromise, which meant there was always water on the tunnel floor. A disastrous blowout did occur in July, 1880; a door in the air lock jammed and twenty men drowned. By 1882, partly as a result of the costs of the accident, Haskin was out of funds. In 1888, a British company, with Great-

CINCINNATI

BROOKLYN

GEORGE WASHINGTON

GOLDEN GATE

VERRAZANO-NARROWS

*Of all engineering works, none had had such enduring popular appeal as the suspension bridge, and the bigger the better. The crowning achievement of the years between the World Wars was New York City's George Washington Bridge, designed by Othmar Ammann. By far the most stupendous suspension bridge that had ever been built, it was almost double the length of any previous bridge and the first of the monumental modern spans.*

head as consulting engineer, tried to finish the tunnel, but it also was insolvent by 1891. An American company finally completed the tunnel in 1906 to serve commuters in a rapid-transit system.

The Hudson Tube, as it came to be called, soon had neighbors. A parallel tube was begun the same year, and the Pennsylvania Railroad tunneled under the Hudson to Pennsylvania Station in 1910. Another railroad tube lay under the East River, linking Manhattan with Long Island. Eventually there were to be twenty tunnels connecting Manhattan under its several rivers with its neighbors.

In 1906, a young engineer fresh out of Harvard was at work on one of the first of the East River tunnels. "I am going into tunnel work," Clifford M. Holland had told a classmate, "and I am going to put a lot more into it than I'll ever be paid for." By the time he was thirty-one, Holland had charge of four subway tunnels—all being constructed at once—under the East River. He was constantly underground, supervising the work, answering questions, calmly solving emergencies. He impressed older colleagues with his expertness; he also impressed the sand hogs, ordinarily disdainful of their white-collar supervisors. "That bird could come down here blindfolded in the dark and tell us if we was going wrong!" one of them remarked.

To those who knew him, therefore, it came as no surprise when the young engineer was put in charge of the first vehicular tunnel to be dug under the Hudson. A two-state commission favored a tunnel rather than a bridge for the first automobile link between New York and New Jersey, and they accepted Holland's plan over all others, including one submitted by the venerable George Goethals.

Holland's plan called for twin tubes, each thirty feet in diameter, more than a mile and a half long, dipping seventy-two feet below high-water level. From his knowledge and experience Holland knew that he could dig the enormous tunnel, but a greater challenge arose from the nature of the vehicles that would use it. Automobiles emitted noxious fumes and, worse, deadly carbon monoxide. Holland went to Europe to study the ventilation problem; he called in experts from the U.S. Bureau of Mines; he sponsored research projects at Yale and the University of Illinois. At length he had his answer: four ten-story ventilation towers, two on each shore, containing powerful electric fans. The fans would pump air into the cylindrical tunnel, through the space under the roadway, at the rate of nearly four million cubic feet a minute. Vents at curbside would carry the air up into the vehicular area, and exhaust fans in the ventilation towers would suck it out through vents in the roof of the vehicular area. With this powerful system, air would be changed every ninety seconds. (Traffic has increased during the forty years since the tunnel was opened, but the rate of air renewal is still the same.)

The tunnel itself would be dug by the proven methods of shielding and compressed air, and lined with 115,000 tons of curved, cast-iron sections and 130,000 cubic yards of concrete. Work began late in 1920, with headings

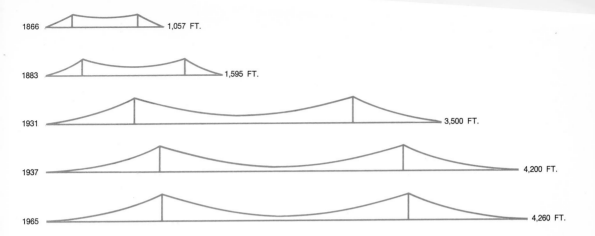

1866 — 1,057 FT.

1883 — 1,595 FT.

1931 — 3,500 FT.

1937 — 4,200 FT.

1965 — 4,260 FT.

eastward from Jersey City and westward from lower Manhattan. Most of the digging was through silt, but toward the New York shore lay nearly a thousand feet of solid rock, which had to be blasted. At last the headings met on October 29, 1924. There was to have been an elaborate celebration of the event, with President Coolidge, by remote control, firing the final blast. But the day passed somberly —in honor of Clifford M. Holland, 41-year-old engineer, who had died two days earlier. Holland had been warned not to overtax himself, but the advice was inconsonant with his way of doing things and he paid the price for ignoring it. A few weeks after his death the tunnel was officially named in his honor. Holland's successor, Milton Freeman, died after five months on the job; Ole Singstad, the third chief engineer, finished the work.

On November 12, 1927, the tunnel officially opened. Twenty thousand people walked the length of the gleaming, white-tiled corridor during the first hour; another fifty-one thousand drove through it. They were not unmindful of the fact that this was a great engineering feat, setting a record for length among the world's then few vehicular tunnels. But America was growing accustomed to superlatives, even to records that were short-lived. Lindbergh flew the Atlantic alone in 1927, and soon there were others outdistancing him. In 1930 the Chrysler Building, a thousand feet tall, then stood as the world's highest skyscraper, but the next year the Empire State Building loomed two hundred feet higher. Also in 1930 the Diablo Dam in the state of Washington

was the world's tallest, but Hoover Dam, completed six years later, was nearly twice as tall.

Under the circumstances, the record length for suspension bridges set by the Roeblings' Brooklyn Bridge could not last forever. Its record tumbled in 1903, when the Williamsburg Bridge was completed with a center span five feet longer than the neighboring Brooklyn Bridge. Bear Mountain Bridge (1924), across the Hudson below West Point, added 32 feet to the record; the Philadelphia-Camden Bridge (1926), another 118 feet; the Ambassador Bridge (1929) at Detroit, 100 feet.

But these were not significant advances; they were rather like the inches that are added to establish a new Olympic broad-jump record. The truly spectacular leap was taken by Othmar H. Ammann in 1931, when he built a suspension bridge across the Hudson at New York. From tower to tower the George Washington Bridge was thirty-five hundred feet long— nearly twice the length of any previous suspension span. The main span of the Golden Gate Bridge, finished six years later, would be seven hundred feet longer, and that of the Verrazano-Narrows Bridge, completed in 1965, would be slightly longer than that. But the really significant achievement was Ammann's George Washington Bridge.

The Panama Canal, the Holland Tunnel, the George Washington Bridge—these were all heady stuff for an America proud of its material accomplishments and convinced of its invincibility in matters technical. "The colossal we do every day" might have been the appropriate slogan.

# IN THE AGE
# OF THE
# AUTOMOBILE

In 1912, a 25-year-old professor of civil engineering at the University of Idaho wrote a letter to Gustav Lindenthal, an eminent bridge builder in New York City. I want to build long-span bridges, said the eager young man, David B. Steinman. Back came the reply: the day of big bridges is over, said Lindenthal, for steel has become too expensive!

Lindenthal's shortsightedness ranks with that of his contemporaries who dismissed the automobile as an insignificant toy. The one case of myopia is related to the other, for the automobile, more than anything else in the twentieth century, was destined to account for the greatest spurt of bridge-building that history has ever seen. The automobile, indeed, would transform the American landscape. For the sake of it, mountains would be torn asunder, the countryside ribboned with concrete and splotched with billboards, and cities subjugated to the demands of traffic.

There were less than a million cars on the road when Lindenthal wrote his reply to Steinman, more than thirty million on the eve of World War II. Today there are nearly one hundred million motor vehicles in the United States; passenger cars alone account for about 730 billion miles of travel every year—almost enough for four round trips to the sun.

In fairness to Lindenthal, it should be recorded that in 1914 he changed his mind and summoned Steinman to New York to become his assistant. Lindenthal had contracts to build two bridges—neither of which, as it happens, had anything to do with automobiles. One was to be a railroad bridge across the Ohio

at Sciotoville, Ohio, a continuous truss 1,550 feet long. The other was a railroad span across the East River in New York, the Hell Gate Bridge, a steel arch 1,017 feet from abutment to abutment.

Gustav Lindenthal was a Moravian-born engineer who immigrated to the United States in his twenties and quickly established his reputation as assistant engineer of construction for the nation's Centennial Exhibition in Philadelphia. For a while he was an engineering consultant in Pittsburgh, where his engineering reputation grew, especially in the field of bridge-building. He moved to New York in the 1890's, served as the city's commissioner of bridges between 1902 and 1903, and then returned to private practice.

The Hell Gate Bridge for which he summoned Steinman's help was Lindenthal's second East River crossing. During his tenure as commissioner, he designed a continuous cantilever bridge to link Manhattan and Queens. When it was opened in 1909, the Queensboro Bridge was the longest cantilever in the United States, with two unequal spans of 1,182 and 984 feet. For some reason, perhaps in order to make his bridge meld more harmoniously with three suspension spans farther south (the Williamsburg, the Manhattan, and the Brooklyn bridges), Lindenthal omitted the usual suspended span in the center and instead joined the cantilever arms directly to each other. This gave the top chord an uninterrupted curve, so that the main spans had the outline of a suspension bridge, but it also made the stresses indeterminate and weakened the spans.

It was Lindenthal's intention to run four tracks of the recently opened subway line across the Queensboro Bridge, as well as lanes for trolleys and pedestrians. After the Quebec Bridge disaster in 1907, two independent engineering groups were called in to examine the Queensboro's load-bearing capacity. Their reports concurred in finding the bridge inadequate to support its intended load and the number of rapid-transit tracks had to be reduced to two. The other two tracks were diverted to a subway tunnel that was dug under the river one block away, at an additional cost of four million dollars.

Lindenthal had not fully mastered the cantilever form, but neither had other engineers of that time. Unlike Cooper at Quebec, Lindenthal survived his mistake with his reputation more or less unblemished, because the Queensboro was clearly an exception to his rule of high quality, and the errors that went into its design had not become fatal. The structure was excessively heavy: to build 3,724 feet of bridge required more than fifty thousand tons of steel, or about thirteen and a half tons per linear foot. "My God," said a consulting architect viewing the finished bridge; "it's a blacksmith's shop!"

With the young Steinman supervising construction, clambering over high steel day after day, Lindenthal, then in his sixties, took charge of the desk details of his Sciotoville and Hell Gate bridges. Both spans were engineering triumphs. The Sciotoville Bridge, completed in 1917, held the record as the world's longest continuous truss (a form that had been

rarely used in the United States because of the difficulty of calculating its stresses) until 1935, the year of Lindenthal's death. And the Hell Gate, which held the world's record for steel arches almost as many years, had a gracefulness of form that disguised its incredible strength. It was designed to carry a total load (live and dead) of seventy-six thousand pounds per linear foot—more than any other bridge ever built.

Though he built record-winning spans in three of the major bridge forms (cantilever, continuous truss, and steel arch), Lindenthal's career-long dream was to build a gigantic suspension bridge across the Hudson River at midtown Manhattan. Even before he left Pittsburgh he had a New York bridge company interested in his plans, and in subsequent years he refined and expanded these into a bridge that would give new meaning to the term "mass transit."

He envisioned a double-decked structure with a center span of more than three thousand feet. That was fantastic enough, considering the fact that the Williamsburg Bridge, then the world's longest suspension span, was sixteen hundred feet long from tower to tower. But Lindenthal also planned to make his bridge 235 feet wide—to carry twelve rapid-transit tracks, sixteen vehicle lanes, two bus lanes, two sets of trolley tracks, and two sidewalks. From an engineering point of view, the bridge was perfectly feasible. Its cost, however, was prohibitive and no company could be found to take it beyond the project stage. This was probably just as well. The present

*Othmar H. Ammann's George Washington Bridge is a landmark in more ways than length. When its second deck was added, 30 years after the first, its 220-ton sections, 72 of them, were raised and riveted into place while traffic flowed unceasingly on the deck above. David B. Steinman's crowning achievement is the Mackinac Bridge (opposite), the world's longest suspension bridge, anchorage to anchorage. Its cost also was outsized: $99,800,000.*

crowded network of tunnels and bridges crossing the Hudson at least disperses travelers in different areas of the city. Lindenthal's all-purpose portal at midtown would have been a traffic bottleneck of stupefying proportions.

Lindenthal was denied the colossal monument to his genius, but he left a legacy of incalculable importance to engineering through his two assistants: David B. Steinman and Othmar H. Ammann.

Both worked with Lindenthal on the Hell Gate Bridge. In later years they were competitors who respected each other's work but could never be friends. Ammann was a severe and urbane Swiss, well-to-do and gentlemanly, as precise as a Swiss watch, who decided early in his career to specialize in big bridges and came to America to do so. Steinman was a poor-born New Yorker, given to passionate enthusiasms, disposed to write poetry, who grew up in the shadow of the Brooklyn Bridge and worshiped it and its builders. His *Suspension Bridges and Cantilevers*, a book published when he was twenty-five, was a commercial success. When he joined Lindenthal three years later, Steinman had already built his first bridge: a log structure, forty feet long, across an Idaho creek. He and a troop of Boy Scouts built it by hand, using no nails, employing a cantilever of Steinman's own design. It was a remarkable little bridge, and it rated an article and photograph in *Engineering News*.

The work with Lindenthal on the Hell Gate Bridge was instructive, and Steinman and Ammann subsequently built important arch spans of their own around New York. Am-

mann's bridge between Bayonne, New Jersey, and Staten Island, built in 1931, is, at 1,652 feet, the longest arch span in the world. Like the Hell Gate, its overhead arch rises in a parabolic curve above the deck, which is suspended from it by steel-wire hangers.

Steinman's Henry Hudson Bridge, over the Harlem River separating Manhattan from the Bronx, was opened in 1936, but its design had been proposed by Steinman nearly thirty years before—in his graduation thesis at Columbia. It is a single arch, with the 800-foot-long deck mounted on top, like the Eads Bridge. The span was originally intended as a single deck with six highway lanes, since Steinman guessed that some six million cars would use the bridge in a year. It was hard to be sure, however, since each car would be charged a toll to cross it, there was a free bridge not far away, and these were Depression years. The number of lanes was cut to four, but Steinman provided in the plans for an upper deck, just in case. Within a month of the bridge's opening, the press of traffic was so great that the upper deck was begun immediately. Within four years the bridge was carrying more than thirteen million cars a year, and their tolls soon paid for its construction.

But it was as masters of the suspension bridge that both men won their chief renown. Each had that intuitive command of the design and material which is an essential ingredient for a successful bridge engineer. Steinman probably had the most work in the idiom, with a practice that stretched from the Atlantic to the Pacific coasts and brought him com-

missions and fame in many countries overseas. It fell to Ammann, however, to take the most significant step in suspension-bridge engineering, and in doing so to realize Lindenthal's old dream.

In 1923, Ammann was bridge engineer for the Port of New York Authority, a position which gave him a chance to argue once again for a bridge that would cross the Hudson. He suggested an uptown site, however, where the height of the Palisades of New Jersey would be counterbalanced by that of the highest ground on Manhattan Island. After four years of negotiation and planning, work began on the bridge that would be nearly twice as long as any suspension span previously built: the George Washington Bridge.

Ammann's design called for a main span of 3,500 feet, with anchor spans of only 610 and 650 feet, requiring an unusually shallow curve to the cable. The deck, 119 feet wide, carried eight vehicle lanes and was suspended from four cables, each a yard thick and nearly a mile long. The towers, rising 635 feet above the water, were vast steel trusses. Cass Gilbert, the consulting architect, intended to envelop them in concrete and add a granite facing, but the Port Authority, its eyes on the money box, turned him down. For economic reasons, therefore, the towers ended up following the aesthetic dictum that form should follow function, that a completed structure should honestly express the materials which support it. The exposed steel trussing clearly expresses the awesome strength of the towers of the George Washington Bridge; it is another question, on which critics disagree, whether the towers can be called beautiful.

It was Ammann's intention to place a second deck beneath the main one for rapid-transit vehicles, and to use 26-foot-deep stiffening trusses between the decks to give the bridge stability. But financial problems arose, and Ammann had to complete the bridge (in 1931) without the second deck and trusses. It was a daring decision, but based on his precise knowledge of the characteristics of the bridge. Eventually, in 1962, the trussing was added along with a second deck carrying another six vehicle lanes. Aided by an elaborate system of ramp approaches on each shore, the fourteen lanes of the George Washington Bridge now carry nearly sixty million vehicles a year across the Hudson River.

The George Washington Bridge proved the case for colossal suspension bridges, the automobile made the case worth proving, and the clinking silver at the toll booths made such projects appealing, even in the midst of the Depression. San Franciscans came to favor a bridge, long talked of, that would link their city with Marin County across the Golden Gate entrance to the harbor. The center span would be seven hundred feet longer than the George Washington's, but that added to the challenge. There were other things to worry about: the fog and high winds, the choppy Pacific and its swift currents, the depth to which foundations would have to be sunk, the ship traffic that would add to the usual hazards of construction. Joseph B. Strauss, the 62-year-old chief engineer, coped with them all successfully. Construction began in 1933 and was triumphantly completed four years later; San Francisco celebrated the opening of the Golden Gate Bridge with a week-long fiesta.

Othmar Ammann was one of the consulting engineers for the Golden Gate; so was Leon S. Moisseiff, a Russian-born bridge engineer who had helped design the Manhattan suspension bridge between New York and Brooklyn before the First World War, and served as consultant on almost every important American bridge project thereafter. Following the trend toward making the suspension form more graceful by decreasing the depth of stiffening members, Moisseiff designed an elegant bridge—long, light, and slender—across the Narrows of Puget Sound at Tacoma, Washington. When opened in July, 1940, it was the third longest suspension span in the world—2,800 feet.

By this time everyone knew that suspension bridges were flexible and that they were also safe; so as the Tacoma Narrows Bridge dipped and swayed high above the water, people simply christened the span "Galloping Gertie." Workmen finishing the steelwork had complained of seasickness from the constant motion. Once the span was completed, it rapidly became a tourist attraction: motorists went out of their way to go for a ride on it.

On November 7, 1940, four months after the Tacoma Bridge opened, a newspaperman drove onto it; his dog was at his side to share the fun of the experience. The day was windy, though at about forty miles per hour the winds were far from terrifying. The bridge, however, was heaving up and down in regular three-foot

waves, and the authorities, alarmed, closed it to traffic. A third of the way across, the reporter, alone on the bridge, dared drive no farther. Galloping Gertie was no longer just rippling but twisting and turning in a series of violent vibrations that steadily increased in depth. The reporter got out of his car; his dog, frozen with terror, refused to leave and had to be abandoned. The reporter tried to run but could not keep his footing. Falling to his knees, he began crawling back to the shore, clinging to the curb, as the great bridge pitched up and down. Bleeding, he made it to safety, then watched as the deck lifted and writhed, finally to rip from its suspenders and plunge into Puget Sound.

A bridge does not die without an autopsy by civil engineers, and the investigation that followed the Tacoma Narrows catastrophe revealed how thoroughly John Roebling's admonitions about stiffening had been forgotten. It also revealed how little was known about aerodynamics, the science of gases in motion. Wind wrecked the Tacoma Bridge, and a basic flaw in its design, studies revealed, was the stiffening of the deck by means of solid plate girders. To the wind, a steel truss is a sieve but a girder is a solid wall, and the oscillations generated by the wind, eddying around the girders, proved fatal to the bridge. Ammann, who had just supervised construction of the Bronx-Whitestone Bridge in New York with girders, quickly replaced them with trusses.

Steinman had long been interested in aerodynamics and in 1918, at the City College of New York, had introduced the subject into the

Beneath the turbulent waters of
Chesapeake Bay workmen complete
the interior of a tunnel section
in the 17.6-mile-long bridge-
tunnel complex. The sections
were assembled in shipyards
in Texas, then towed over a
thousand miles to the Chesapeake,
where they were floated out to
trenches already dug in the bay
floor and very carefully lowered
into place. The diagram shows
the tunnels surfacing at four
man-made islands and joining the
trestled bridges over the water.

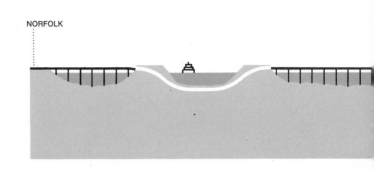

NORFOLK

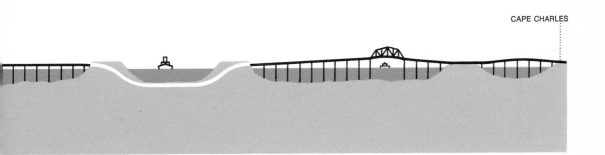

American curriculum for the first time. When two of his own suspension spans at the Thousand Islands, in upper New York State, developed undulations somewhat similar to those that later struck the Tacoma Bridge, he had stabilized them with cable stays. Before Gertie fell, he offered to consult with Moisseiff on corrective measures, and though he was turned down, he later took pains to exonerate the older man in his writings, placing the blame instead on the whole engineering profession. In the wake of the disaster, however, Steinman began a thorough study of the aerodynamics of suspension bridges.

His reward came in 1954: the task of spanning the icy, gale-blown Straits of Mackinac that separate upper and lower Michigan. For it, Steinman designed the longest of all suspension bridges in over-all length—8,614 feet from anchorage to anchorage, five miles including approaches. To resist the pressure and weight of ice and snow over the long winters, Steinman made his piers and anchorages exceptionally strong, using 890,000 tons of concrete and steel. The deck he stiffened by 38-foot trusses, exactly one-hundredth of the main-span length. In deference to the wind he made two of his four vehicle lanes with open-grid roadbeds and, on both sides of the bridge, left a ten-foot gap between the edge of the deck and the stiffening trusses.

The Mackinac Bridge was completed in 1957 and Steinman died in 1960. Just the year before, his rival Ammann had begun work on a bridge Steinman had long hoped to construct —the longest and heaviest suspension span in

the world. Like the Golden Gate, whose length it has surpassed by just sixty feet, the Verrazano-Narrows Bridge is an awesome gateway to a great port. Ships entering New York Harbor pass beneath the monumental span, which is supported by gray-painted towers as high as a sixty-story skyscraper. The Verrazano Bridge deals only in superlatives: everything about it is bigger, stronger, or longer than other bridges. Partly it is big just for the sake of it. When Ammann died in 1965, his crowning achievement, in a sense, was not the vast structure opened just the year before, but the pioneering leap forward thirty-five years earlier: the George Washington Bridge.

More than anything else, the Verrazano-Narrows Bridge is a monument to the unrelenting pressure of the automobile to transform the American landscape. By the time a second deck is added, it is expected to carry forty-eight million motor vehicles a year. Most of the great bridges around New York had been built to transport people into and out of the city; the Verrazano-Narrows Bridge was built so that motorists could avoid the congested city altogether on their north-south trips along the Atlantic Coast. Like the limited-access highways and the beltways that loop around major cities, it was put there to fulfill the American motorist's dream: a trip from here to there, anywhere, with the speedometer planted at seventy and the view from behind the steering wheel an unchanging, unresisting band of concrete.

Far to the south of the Verrazano-Narrows Bridge is another engineering marvel, a structure of a different kind in quite a different setting, which is just as fully dedicated to the demands of the automobile. The Chesapeake Bay Bridge-Tunnel, begun in 1960 and completed four years later, became the final link in a coastal highway that now extends from the Canadian border to Key West, Florida. This complex route over and under Chesapeake Bay is seventeen and a half miles long, which makes it the longest vehicular crossing in the world. It connects the Tidewater area of Virginia—Norfolk and Portsmouth—to the Delmarva peninsula, an area of rural, underdeveloped America shared by Delaware, Maryland, and Virginia.

The waters of Chesapeake Bay are tugged back and forth by the powerful tides of the Atlantic, often topped by huge waves driven by fierce winds. Below the surface is swirling silt and mud; the bottom sediments are soft and bedrock is sometimes two thousand feet below the water's surface. Twelve miles of trestle highway had to be supported on concrete piles, driven deep into the muck, often more than a hundred feet but, of course, far above the bedrock. A floating pile driver with telescoping metal legs was built at a cost of one and a half million dollars. With its feet planted firmly on the bottom of the bay, it could sink piles up to 170 feet long, weighing 75 tons. Behind the pile driver followed another complicated machine, nicknamed the "Two-headed Monster." Mounted on the piles, it leveled them with its forward head, then capped them with its rear head, ready to receive the roadbed, which was laid in slabs by a third

giant machine. These leviathans survived hurricanes and cyclones, though "Big D," as the pile driver was called, capsized in a severe storm in March, 1962, and had to be rebuilt. The two men who were aboard the monster at the time were rescued by a helicopter that braved 50-mile-an-hour winds.

The whole crossing might have been made by bridges, had it not been for the objections of the U.S. Navy, whose Atlantic fleet had its home base in Norfolk, Virginia. Suspension bridges across the navigational channels would not do, said the Navy; if bombed, they would form a serious obstruction to warships. Instead, engineers designed two tunnels, each more than a mile long, which would connect with the trestle sections on four man-made islands in the middle of the bay. Tunneling was done by the trench method, which since the 1930's has largely replaced the old shield-digging method. A dredge plowed a deep trench in the floor of the bay, then huge prefabricated cylinders of steel and concrete were lowered into place and fastened together to form the tunnel. It was delicate work that waited on favorable tides and weather; barges lowered the sections by playing out cable a little at a time, while deep down, where the muddy water was opaque, a diver guided each section to its precise position wholly by his sense of touch. Concrete was poured into hollow walls of each tube to help sink it and give it added strength. When the thirty-seven tube sections were fastened together they were given a burial mound of gravel. Finally, because each section had steel bulkheads to seal it at both ends and keep

it airtight during the sinking, workmen had to cut away the steel to open a continuous passageway between sections.

Building the islands was a fairly uncomplicated but gargantuan task. Rocks were spilled on the bottom of the bay, then their spaces filled with sand, then more rocks, then more sand, in alternate layers until the island stood twenty feet above water level. Sea walls of rock and reinforced concrete afforded protection against violent storms.

At a cost of $140 million, the Chesapeake Bay Bridge-Tunnel fulfilled the purpose for which it was intended: a two-hour improvement in the journey between New York and Norfolk. And eventually it may, to the tune of the internal combustion engine, transform the Delmarva peninsula from a sleepy backwater to an extension of the megalopolis that now runs from Boston to Washington, D.C.

The automobile has been an agent of change of overwhelming importance in the twentieth century, but we need to be reminded that other forms of transportation, and other routes to carry them, continue to play a part in America's development. Noteworthy is the St. Lawrence Seaway, opened in 1959, the first large waterway built since the Panama Canal. The St. Lawrence River was a natural link between the Great Lakes and the Atlantic Ocean, but Nature also endowed the river with treacherous rapids in three different places. Early in the twentieth century, Canada made the river navigable for canalboats part of the way by installing a series of twenty-two locks. But men of vision sought a bolder solution: a route for large ocean vessels from the Atlantic clear to the ports of the Great Lakes. Finally, in 1954, the United States and Canada agreed to undertake the project jointly, to complete a passageway 183 miles long by dredging the river, damming it in three places, and building forty-five miles of canal with seven locks to bypass the rapids.

The obstacles surmounted in five years of construction were many. Millions of tons of greasy clay—"blue goop," it was called—had to be excavated. Sloshing out of dredge buckets and penetrating the parts of all equipment, the clay would turn rubbery and even brittle when exposed to the sun and air, until rain turned it soupy or ice froze it. The nineteenth-century builders of the Erie Canal would have marveled at the huge machinery that handled it; one 650-ton leviathan, nicknamed "the Gentleman," bit up the ground in 25-ton mouthfuls. In a six-month period, two million tons of earth were removed from the new ship channel. The digging for one set of locks required the removal of three million tons of a flinty rock that quickly blunted every tool used to attack it. The engineers turned to a new technique called jet-burning; they disintegrated the rock by firing jet flames into it. In ten hours the jet torch could sink a blast hole one hundred feet deep.

The jet torch gave the ultimate touch of modernity to the building of the St. Lawrence Seaway. It was not to be the last word in hard-rock excavation, however, for laser beams, beams of electrons, and atomic energy have since proved useful. The Space Age has left its mark on civil engineering in other ways. The computer now solves equations for stress and load-bearing capacities; it can simulate real conditions of use and tell designers where to put toll booths and how many to keep open, at what times, for smoothest flow of traffic.

The remarkable new synthetic materials that have found their way into the American household have, not surprisingly, also found use in civil engineering. Canals can be housed in watertight channels lined with vinyl sheeting; in California, suspension cables are being wrapped in acrylic resin coverings that do away with the need for constant painting. In the East, two bridges on the New York State Thruway are made of concrete deck beams glued together with epoxy resins and mounted on glued piles spliced with hot epoxy. The method cost about four dollars a foot less than a conventional bridge, but the saving in time was even more impressive—about a year. Epoxy is also coming into use as a long-lasting component of road surfaces.

Aluminum, that metal as familiar to housewives as it is to airplane builders, has not yet been completely successful in bridge-building. But an all-aluminum arch over the Saguenay River in Quebec has satisfactorily withstood heavy traffic and severe winters since 1946. It needs no painting and weighs only 190 tons as compared with 430, had it been built of steel. Ways have also been found to make steel bridges lighter and hence less costly. One of the most successful is the orthotropic bridge, made of steel-plate girders supported on columns, in which the girders themselves form the

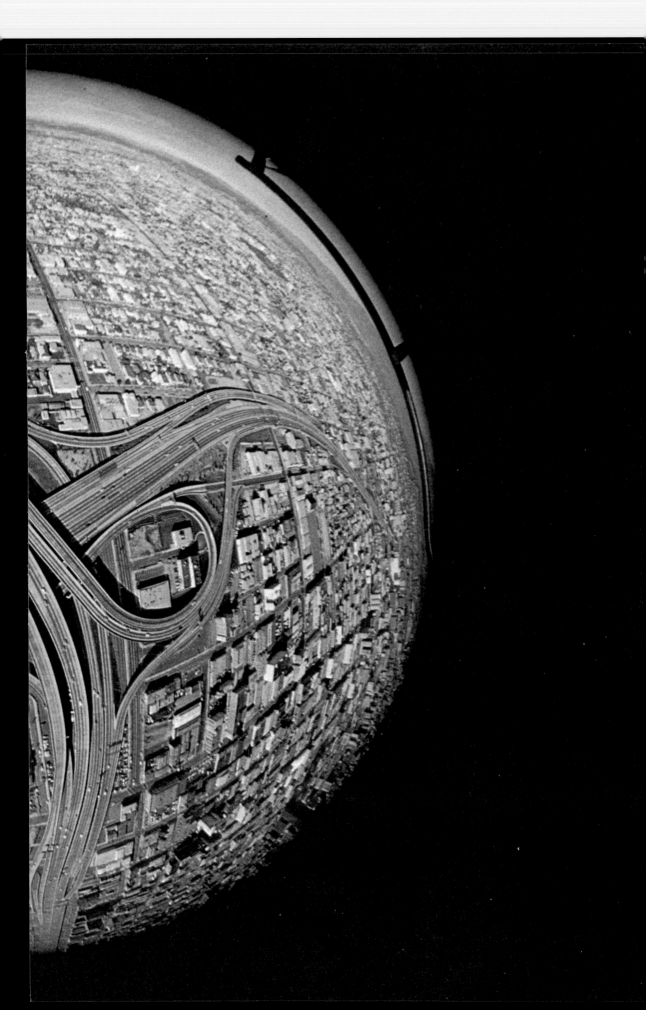

roadbed, with only a light road surfacing to prevent cars from slipping on the steel.

Two-thirds along in the twentieth century, questions of how we build are less important than other questions: What are we building, and why? Since 1956 the United States has completed more than forty thousand miles of interstate highways, bringing Albert Gallatin's old dream of a national network of roads close to fruition. (Even Gallatin's perception that such a network would have great military value has been realized; a standard specification for these new roads is that they be able to bear the weight of sixty-ton tanks.) But the achievements have been a mixed blessing.

Neighborhoods have been torn down to make room for highways slicing through our cities; some have simply withered under the concrete umbrella of an elevated expressway. The superhighway devours land in an unprecedented way; it demands widely curved ramps, huge clover-leafs, intricate tiers of overpasses and underpasses. The George Washington Bridge, when it was built, was a symptom of what the automobile was doing; the elaborate approaches to the bridge accounted for more than a third of its cost.

But doubts about the new American landscape go deeper than the resentment some are beginning to feel about the tyranny of the automobile. The engineering achievements that mark the landscape—the bridges of steel, the skyscrapers with skins of aluminum and glass, the roadways of concrete—do not exhilarate, as once they might have, partly because engineers, having proven so often and in so

many ways that they can build the colossal, invite no surprises about what more they can accomplish. No one doubts that larger canals, taller buildings, bigger bridges, longer tunnels can be built. The obstacles that now challenge the American spirit are primarily social, not physical. If the master builder who completes a colossal bridge is robbed of the glory due him, it is because slums have still to be eradicated, violence subdued, urban life made comfortable, justice universalized. And, sad to say, engineering feats have often been irrelevant to, and sometimes detrimental to, progress in these areas.

The bridges, canals, and tunnels discussed in this book have been triumphs *of* the human spirit because of the obstacles men overcame in building them; tomorrow's structures must be triumphs *for* the human spirit, built to enhance life for man in all respects. The structures may be of a wholly different order: radically new systems for transporting commuters with great speed and comfort; cities that are planned as "total environments" and built from scratch; perhaps technological innovations that eliminate the need for urban concentration altogether. These will be built, not by engineers working alone as masters of their specialty, but by synthesizers and planners who take into consideration the whole range of human needs and technical possibilities.

The great American bridges, canals, and tunnels will continue to have a special significance—reminding us of what the human spirit can accomplish, engendering optimism about tasks that lie ahead.

# APPENDIX

# CHRONOLOGY

**1800** *America builds her first canal, the Santee Canal in South Carolina. Length, 22 miles, with 13 brick-and-stone locks. In use until 1850.*

**1806** *Permanent Bridge built over the Schuylkill River at Philadelphia. A covered wooden structure of three spans, it was one of the first important trussed-arch bridges. Length, 550 feet. Timothy Palmer, designer.*

**1812** *The Colossus crosses the Schuylkill, also at Philadelphia. A single-span, trussed arch, 340 feet long, it was, in its time and for years afterward, the longest timber span in the U.S. Designed by Lewis Wernwag.*

**1816** *The world's first wire-suspension bridge for foot traffic spans the Schuylkill at Phila-delphia. Length, 408 feet. Built by Josiah White and Erskine Hazard.*

**1821** *The first tunnel in the U.S., a canal tunnel, is constructed on the Schuylkill Navigation Canal near Auburn, Pennsylvania. Length, 450 feet.*

**1825** *The Erie Canal completed. Then the longest man-made water-way, it stretched 363 miles, from Albany to Buffalo. Built under Benjamin Wright's direction.*

**1828** *Construction of the Balti-more and Ohio Railroad begins at Baltimore. The first railroad in the U.S. opened to public traffic.*

**1828** *The Delaware and Hudson Canal extends 106 miles from Honesdale, Pennsylvania, to Kingston, New York, connecting the Delaware and Hudson rivers. Built under the direction of Benjamin Wright.*

**1830** *Commissioned by B & O Railroad, Lewis Wernwag spans the Monocacy River in Maryland with the first timber railroad bridge in the U.S.*

**1833** *The Allegheny Tunnel, 701 feet long, cuts through a mountain near Johnstown, Pennsylvania. Built by Allegheny Portage Railroad, it was the first railway tunnel in the U.S.*

**1834** *The Pennsylvania Canal links Philadelphia with Pitts-burgh in a 400-mile complex of railroads and canals.*

**1836** *Lewis Wernwag builds a major timber bridge at Harpers Ferry to carry B & O Railroad and a roadway across the Potomac River and C & O Canal.*

**1842** *A wire-cable suspension bridge, the first for road traffic in America, replaces Wernwag's Colossus. Its clear span measured 358 feet. Designed by Charles Ellet.*

**1845** *World's first suspension aqueduct and John Roebling's first suspension structure crosses Allegheny River at Pittsburgh. Holding 2,100 tons of water, it carried the boats of the Pennsylvania Canal.*

**1846** *The Monongahela Bridge, a suspension span, crosses the Monongahela River at Pitts-burgh. Total length, 1,500 feet. John Roebling, designer.*

**1848** *Charles Ellet's foot-bridge, a light suspension span 770 feet long and 7 feet wide, crosses the gorge at Niagara.*

**1848** *The Starrucca Viaduct, built by the New York and Erie Railroad, crosses a valley near Susquehanna, Pennsylvania. It was the first bridge in U.S. to use concrete in the piers. James P. Kirkwood, engineer.*

**1848** *The Illinois and Michigan Canal connects La Salle, Illinois, with Chicago, completing the all-water route from the Gulf of Mexico to Lake Michigan.*

**1849** *The Wheeling Bridge, a suspension bridge with a record span of 1,010 feet, crosses the Ohio River at Wheeling, Virginia (now West Virginia). Designed by Charles Ellet.*

**1850** *The Chesapeake and Ohio Canal, originally planned to link Chesapeake Bay with the Ohio River, comes to a construction halt at Cumberland, Maryland, as a result of competition from the Baltimore and Ohio Railroad.*

**1851** *At Harpers Ferry, Wendel Bollman replaces a collapsed span of Wernwag's timber bridge with a cast- and wrought-iron truss structure capable of supporting more than one ton per foot of bridge. The first major Bollman truss.*

**1852** *An all-iron railroad bridge built by the B & O Railroad crosses the Monongahela River at Fairmont, Virginia (now West Virginia). It was the first major bridge to use the special trusses designed by Albert Fink.*

**1855** *An 821-foot-long railroad bridge spans the Niagara gorge. The first railway suspension bridge in the world. John Roebling, engineer.*

**1856** *The Wabash and Erie Canal, the longest (452 miles) canal in the U.S., links Toledo, Ohio, with Evansville, Indiana.*

**1859** *The Louisville and Nashville Railroad constructs an iron truss bridge across the Green River in Kentucky. With five spans totaling 1,000 feet, it is the longest and perhaps most spectacular iron bridge in America to date. Engineer, Albert Fink.*

**1864** *The first long-span truss bridge (320 feet) is built by the Pittsburgh, Cincinnati, Chicago, and St. Louis Railroad over the Ohio River at Steubenville. J. H. Linville, engineer.*

**1867** *The Cincinnati Bridge, a suspension bridge across the Ohio River, sets a world record with a clear span of 1,057 feet. Engineers, John and Washington Roebling.*

**1870** *Manhattan gets its first subway, an experimental pneumatic tube extending a block and a half under lower Broadway. Design, Alfred Beach.*

**1871** *The first concrete bridge in the U.S., a roadway arch spanning 20 feet, is constructed in Prospect Park, Brooklyn.*

**1874** *The Eads Bridge, a triple-arch bridge totaling 1,500 feet, the first great steel-arch bridge in the U.S., crosses the Mississippi River at St. Louis. Engineer, James B. Eads.*

**1876** *After 20-odd years of setbacks, boring through nearly five miles of solid rock, the Hoosac Tunnel is completed in western Massachusetts. It was the longest American railroad tunnel of its day.*

**1883** *The Brooklyn Bridge, with a span of 1,595 feet, crosses the East River. A pioneer of long-span, steel-wire cable, suspension bridges. Engineers, John and Washington Roebling.*

**1895** *The first large-scale reinforced-concrete bridge in U.S. spans 70 feet to carry a park drive over a through street in Eden Park, Cincinnati.*

**1904** *The Interborough Rapid Transit (IRT) opens as New York's first rapid transit sub-way. Chief engineer, William Barclay Parsons.*

**1906** *After 33 years of construction and innumerable mishaps, the Hudson Tubes, connecting New Jersey and New York, are completed.*

**1909** *The Queensboro Bridge crossing the East River from Manhattan to Long Island City becomes the longest cantilever in the U.S. in its time. Gustav Lindenthal, engineer.*

**1910** *With the opening of Pennsylvania Station, the New York City terminal of the Pennsylvania Railroad, the East and North river tunnels go into service.*

**1914** *After 33 years of stop-and-go construction, the Panama Canal, first attempted by the French, is completed by the U.S. In its time the largest engineering project undertaken by any government, the canal linked the Atlantic and Pacific through the Isthmus of Panama at a cost of $336,650,000 and an estimated 5,300 lives lost through accidents and disease. George Washington Goethals, engineer.*

**1915** *The Tunkhannock Viaduct, built by the Delaware, Lacka-wanna, and Western Railroad, spans 2,375 feet across the Tunkhannock Valley near Scranton, Pennsylvania, and sets the world's record as the largest concrete viaduct. Designed by A. Burton Cohen.*

**1917** *Hell Gate railroad bridge crosses the East River to Long Island. Only 1,042 feet long, it is the heaviest of steel-arch bridges. Gustav Lindenthal, engineer.*

**1917** *The Quebec Bridge crosses the St. Lawrence River. Its 1,800-foot cantilever span is still the longest single, nonsuspension span in the world. E. H. Duggan and Phelps Johnson, designing engineers.*

**1927** *The Holland Tunnel under the Hudson River connects New Jersey and New York. The first automobile tunnel. Chief engineer, Clifford M. Holland.*

**1929** *The New Cascade Tunnel bores through the Cascade Mountains of Washington for eight miles to become America's longest tunnel. Built by the Great Northern Railway.*

**1931** *The George Washington Bridge crosses the Hudson to Fort Lee, New Jersey. With a span of 3,500 feet, it is the longest suspension bridge to date. A lower deck, part of the original design, was added in 1962. Chief engineer, Othmar H. Ammann.*

**1931** *The Bayonne Bridge crosses the Kill van Kull, connecting Staten Island with New Jersey. At 1,652 feet, it is the longest single-span, steel-arch bridge in the world. Othmar H. Ammann and Allston Dana, engineers.*

**1936** The San Francisco-Oakland Bridge provides another link in the Bay area. It is a bridge-tunnel complex that extends for eight miles.

**1936** The Huey P. Long Bridge built over the Mississippi at New Orleans. The low level of the land necessitated long rail approaches and, at 22,996 feet, it is the longest continuous steel bridge in the world. Modjeski, Masters, and Chase, engineers.

**1937** The Lincoln Tunnel becomes the second subaqueous tunnel to connect New York and New Jersey. Two tubes have since been added, making it the only three-tube vehicular tunnel.

**1937** The Golden Gate Bridge in San Francisco, spanning 4,200 feet, is the longest suspension bridge in the U.S. in its time. Joseph B. Strauss, chief engineer.

**1939** The Bronx-Whitestone Bridge, a suspension bridge with a main span of 2,300 feet, crosses the East River. Othmar H. Ammann and Allston Dana, chief engineers.

**1940** The Tacoma Narrows Bridge crosses Puget Sound in Washington. Known as Galloping Gertie, this 2,800-foot-long suspension bridge collapsed four months after opening. It was replaced and reopened in 1950.

**1950** The Brooklyn Battery Tunnel connects Brooklyn and Manhattan at the junction of upper New York Bay and the East River.

**1951** The Delaware Memorial Bridge crosses the Delaware River to connect New Jersey and Delaware. Total length, 3.5 miles. (A twin bridge beside it was opened to traffic in 1968.)

**1955** The Tappan Zee Bridge crosses the Hudson River at Tarrytown, New York. It uses several types of spans, including the world's heaviest cantilever.

**1957** Crossing the Mackinac Strait, a narrow waterway that connects Lake Huron and Lake Michigan, the Mackinac Bridge becomes the world's third longest clear-span suspension bridge and the longest span from anchorage to anchorage (8,614 feet). Engineered by David B. Steinman.

**1959** The St. Lawrence Seaway connects Montreal with the Great Lakes, providing a marine route from the Atlantic to the western end of Lake Superior.

**1964** The Chesapeake Bay Bridge-Tunnel, an ocean highway complex of bridges and tunnels, spans the mouth of Chesapeake Bay. Total length is 23 miles, 17 of which are traveled over or under water.

**1965** The Verrazano-Narrows Bridge, connecting Brooklyn and Staten Island, has the longest clear span to date of any type of bridge: 4,260 feet.

# MR. BEACH'S
# PNEUMATIC SECRET

Alfred Ely Beach, the 44-year-old publisher of *Scientific American* magazine and avid part-time inventor, submitted a petition in 1868 for a postal dispatch charter in the City of New York. The charter was granted and Beach, without disclosing his real plan, proceeded to build New York's first subway. Its site was 21 feet beneath Broadway, between Warren and Murray streets. The tunnel itself was 9 feet in diameter, 312 feet long, and held one cylindrical car capable of going about 10 miles an hour. A giant 100-horsepower blower propelled the vehicle along a track until it reached the far end, where the fan, reversed by a trip wire, slowed the car to a stop and then pulled it back the other way.

The building of the tunnel, under the supervision of Beach's 21-year-old son, was entirely nocturnal and kept in great secrecy. The work took a total of 58 nights to complete, but it would be another two years before New Yorkers would even know of its existence.

Beach's greatest contribution to the technology of tunnel construction was his shield, hydraulically driven, which looked something like an open-ended tin can and was propelled by pistons that drove it through the earth. Dirt removal and bricklaying went on inside the shield, affording the workers complete protection against cave-ins.

But why all the secrecy? The reason in a word was Tweed. Beach, a man who also understood political engineering, realized that to build his subway without submitting to Tammany blackmail would be an impossibility. Moreover, he decked out his tunnel in finery in order to win public confidence. Thus, in 1870, when the subway was unveiled, William Marcy Tweed and city officials were thrown into a rage. The next year, Governor John T. Hoffman, a Tammany stooge, vetoed Beach's charter in favor of Boss Tweed's counterproposal for a costly elevated railway. But when Tweed was indicted and Hoffman defeated for re-election, John A. Dix, the new governor, signed the charter for the pneumatic subway in 1873. The stock exchange collapse of that year forced Beach to withdraw from the project, and his subway was sealed up and forgotten. From then on Beach devoted himself to publishing and did not live to see New York achieve his dream.

In 1912, workmen digging the new BMT tunnel unexpectedly broke into Beach's subway and found the little car sitting on its tracks, the whole tunnel still remarkably intact. Today the Beach tunnel is part of the BMT's City Hall station, where a plaque commemorates Beach's pioneering and maverick achievement.

The elegance of New York's first
subway will probably never be
surpassed. The décor of Beach's
tunnel platform (below, left)
included fine paintings, frescoed
walls, a grand piano, a
fountain, and a goldfish tank—
bringing the total private
expenditure for the tunnel to
$350,000. Overshadowed by all
this was Beach's substantial contribution to engineering, his
method of tunnel construction:
the hydraulic shield (below) driven
by individually controlled
pistons, would later be used
for construction of London's
Thames, Glasgow's Clyde, and
New York's Hudson tunnels.

# THE ESSENTIALS
# OF BRIDGE BUILDING

**THE BASIC FACTORS** to consider in bridge engineering can be illustrated with a simple plank put across a small creek. If the plank is too thin in relation to its length, it will sag; if it is too long in relation to its strength, it will collapse of its own weight, which is known as its *dead load*. A weight placed at the middle of the plank (yourself, for example) will make it sag still more (you are the *live load*); and if you walk about some, the plank will begin bouncing under you, illustrating the effect of a *moving live load*. And with or without you on it, a plank can be set to shaking by a strong wind; so the *wind load* is another factor to be taken into account.

SIMPLE SPAN

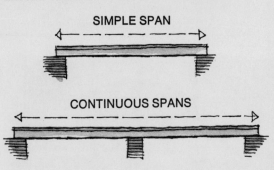

CONTINUOUS SPANS

**THE DISTANCE** a bridge extends between two supports is called the *span*. The drawings show the difference between a *simple span* and a *continuous span*. (Generally speaking, continuous construction requires less material or it enables a span of greater distance.) The man-made supports for a span are known as *piers*—though the outermost supports are commonly called *abutments*— and the location of piers is always a crucial

factor in bridge design. A framework of temporary piers and framing, used to support the incomplete parts of the bridge before they are joined and able to support themselves, is called *falsework*. The use of falsework is not always possible, due to the swiftness of a river current or because it would obstruct river traffic.

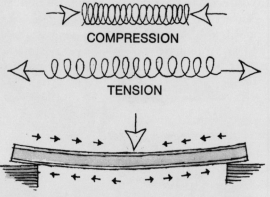

COMPRESSION

TENSION

**THE FORCES** that act on a bridge result in *stresses* in its parts or *members*. There are two principal types of stress, known as *tension*— stretching or pulling apart—and *compression* —squeezing or pushing together. Every member in a bridge must be designed to handle either tension or compression, or a combination of the two.

When you put a weight on a timber that is resting on the ground, the only stress to be reckoned is compression. But if you place the timber between supports, making a *beam* bridge, that same weight creates two stresses. The top of the timber is in compression, but the bottom is in tension, as illustrated above.

**THE MATERIALS** used for bridge-building have ranged from *stone* (which lasts longest) to *wood* (which is inexpensive) to *concrete* (which has great compressive strength, but little tensile strength) to *prestressed concrete* (in which tightly stretched strands of steel wire squeeze the concrete together and give it greater tensile strength) to *iron* (the favorite material for railroad bridges in the 19th century) to *steel* (which has great compressive and tensile strength, can be specially formed to serve innumerable functions, and is the chief building material for most modern bridges).

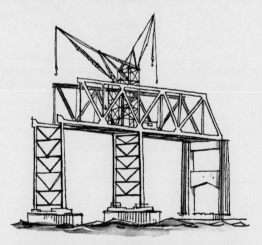

Among the most familiar of steel bridges is the *truss*, a structure built up of individual members arranged in the form of triangles. Truss spans can be simple or continuous; they can be of the *deck type* that you drive over, or the *through type* that you drive through. A bridge such as the Chicago, Burlington, and Quincy Railroad bridge over the Mississippi, at Quincy, Illinois (shown above), is a combination of both.

**THE ASSEMBLING** of a truss is generally done piece-by-piece at the job site, using falsework (as shown left) to support the bottom pieces (or *chords*) while the other members are filled in. But where the use of falsework is impractical, the trusses can be *cantilevered*. This means that as the steel goes out over the water, an equivalent amount of steel is being erected from the piers in the direction of the shorelines.

A cantilever truss bridge consists of side (or *anchor*) spans, cantilever arms, and often a *suspended span*, a truss that hangs from these arms, as illustrated in this sketch. (Such a span is usually assembled on shore, then ferried out to the center of the bridge and hoisted into position.) Below is an arch-form continuous through-truss bridge.

137

1,652-foot main span. It is of the through type, with the roadway hung from the arches. The bridge at left below is the majestic Lewiston-Queenston Bridge over the Niagara River. It is an arch of the deck type, with the arch supporting steel columns that carry the roadway. Its main span is 1,000 feet long.

**ARCH BRIDGES** are among the oldest of bridge types. Ages ago man discovered that long spans of stone are possible because an arch is in compression throughout its entire length and width, thus locking the stones in place. Capable of carrying heavy loads, arches are not only handsome to look at, but well suited for bridging a ravine or chasm with steep, solid walls. Reinforced concrete has been used for single arch spans up to 1,000 feet. The first steel bridge in the U.S., the Eads Bridge at St. Louis, is composed of trussed arches. The Bayonne Bridge (above) crosses the Kill van Kull near New York City and is the world's longest arch bridge, with a

**SIMPLE BEAM BRIDGES** (above) are fast becoming the most familiar type of bridge on the American landscape, as they are being

built in ever increasing numbers along the nation's new superhighways. The supporting beams, laid from pier to pier, are of steel or concrete. With prestressed concrete, spans of 320 feet are possible, but the distance between piers usually is less than 100 feet.

For longer spans—ranging from 200 to 400 feet—*plate-girder* bridges are common. Plate girders are huge beams (such as shown above) that are fabricated by welding, bolting, or riveting together the necessary steel sections. Beams of this kind can be made much deeper and stronger than ordinary rolled beams.

A spectacular example of a plate-girder highway bridge is the Quinnipiac River Bridge on the Connecticut Turnpike at New Haven (shown below). Notice that its plate girders are of the *haunch* design, meaning that they are deeper at the piers, where the extra strength is needed. In addition, they are continuous over several piers.

The girders for the 387-foot main span of this bridge were too big to put up in one piece, so the girders were fabricated in smaller sections. Girders were cantilevered from the piers; then the 107-foot center-pieces were hoisted into place from below by traveler derricks working from the deck. And as with the simple beam bridge, the main supporting members were connected with steel bracing before the paving was added.

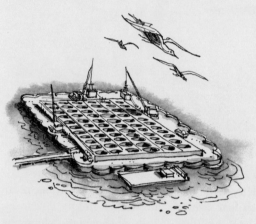

secured with huge bolts and nuts. As cells are matched together and connected, the tower's shafts take shape until they are beyond the reach of derricks working from the ground or water level. Then *creeper travelers*, derricks that climb the steel itself, are put into use, as shown in the sketch at right.

**A MODERN SUSPENSION BRIDGE**, like its early predecessor, the Brooklyn Bridge, begins with the erection of giant towers. But these are of steel, not stone; they are set on mammoth steel piers (above) that go down 100 feet or more, and they are made up of hundreds of box-like *cells*. The sketch below shows bridgemen carefully placing one of the bottom cells on top of a pier, where it will be

**THE TWO SHAFTS** of each tower may be connected in various ways to give them the necessary rigidity. Such connecting members are called *struts*. On top of each tower *saddles* are positioned, and over these are drawn the cable wires. A cable saddle of the type shown here, built for New York's Verrazano-Narrows Bridge, weighs 178 tons. It was placed on top of a tower that rises 690 feet.

(By contrast, the Brooklyn Bridge, which stands only a short distance to the north of the Verrazano, seems almost small-scale. The towers of the Brooklyn Bridge, for instance, are less than half as high, and its span, once the wonder of the world, is only 1,595 feet compared to the immense 4,260-foot sweep of the Verrazano span.)

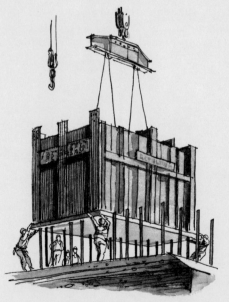

suspension span as San Francisco's Golden Gate Bridge are made up of steel wires just slightly slimmer than a lead pencil, but each is capable of resisting 7,000 pounds of pull. The total length of wire in the cables is about 80,000 miles.

**STRONG SUSPENDER CABLES** are next attached to the main cables. Then the bridge deck is built out to hook onto the suspenders (see sketch at bottom). This is a very delicate process, since the weight must be equalized on both extremes of the main span, as well as on the suspended side spans.

**WITH THE TOWERS UP,** cable-spinning begins, very much along the lines first developed by the Roeblings in the last century. Back and forth go vehicles called *spinning carriages* (right), laying two or more slim steel wires at a time; a number of these wires are then bundled together into what is known as a *strand;* and many such strands make up each of the main cables, which are wrapped with more wire for weather protection.

The main cables of such a popular modern

Once finished, the suspension bridge, despite its immense weight and size, and like no other kind of bridge, has a grace and grandeur seldom equaled by other works of man.

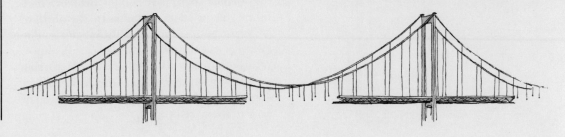

141

# CAUSE
# FOR
# CELEBRATION

*The bands blare, the paraders sweep past, the lofty oratory proclaims it a day to be remembered always; the crowds cheer, the ribbon is cut. . . . The scene has been repeated countless times in America at the opening of a bridge, a tunnel, or a canal. More often than not, the cause for celebration has been a modest work of civil engineering no bigger or more interesting than dozens of other structures in dozens of other sleepy river towns or railroad whistle stops. But the most glorious by far of such "glorious occasions" have been those commemorating what were indeed works of major consequence. The following are brief descriptions of four such occasions —days when everyone on hand had not the slightest doubt that they were witnessing one of history's great events.*

## WEDDING OF
## THE WATERS

The nine-day marathon celebration that opened the Erie Canal began before dawn in Buffalo on October 26, 1825. It was a splendid autumn morning and after a brief ceremony, Governor De Witt Clinton led a group of beaver-hatted dignitaries to the banks of the canal where they boarded the horse-drawn canalboat, *Seneca Chief*, for a 523-mile journey to Sandy Hook, New Jersey, the entrance to New York harbor. On the *Chief*'s deck stood two brightly painted kegs filled with Lake Erie water and small vials of water from twelve of the world's great rivers, all of which was to be poured into the Atlantic in a grand "Wedding of the Waters." The canal formally opened as the official flotilla, lead by the *Chief*, left Buffalo at 10 A.M. A string of booming cannon, placed at 8- to 12-mile intervals along the route, carried the message to Manhattan in just 80 minutes. Brief, noisy stopovers were made along the way and every few miles more craft, including some from foreign nations, fell in behind. One exuberant reporter observed: "Never before was there such a fleet collected, and so superbly decorated, and it is very possible that a display so grand, so beautiful, and we may add sublime, will never again be witnessed."

Leaving the canal at Albany, the boats glided out onto the Hudson where the entire fleet was strung together and tugged straightaway to Sandy Hook by two big steamers. At Sandy

*Crowds turn out to cheer Governor Clinton upon the opening of the Erie Canal in 1825.*

Hook the barges formed up in a huge semicircle and Clinton emptied the kegs of Lake Erie water into the Atlantic to symbolize its union with the Great Lakes. Then he poured the waters of the great rivers, indicating the canal was open to all nations.

The flotilla then backtracked to Manhattan to witness the most spirited celebration the city had ever staged. There were lavish banquets and balls, elaborate floats, parades, and a spectacular fireworks display at City Hall, which was lighted with thousands of candles. There for the occasion were four former presidents—90-year-old John Adams, Jefferson, who was nearing 83, Madison, and Monroe, as well as the man then occupying the White House, John Quincy Adams, and the one who would succeed him, Andrew Jackson. Commemorative medals were presented to the dignitaries and for the rest, ubiquitous hawkers offered everything from dishes to wallpaper decorated with canal scenes. In the eyes of the citizens of such rival cities as Philadelphia, the whole affair seemed just a little absurd, but considering what the canal would mean to New York and to the young nation—which would be far beyond the dreams of even the most ardent canal enthusiasts—there was every reason to celebrate.

## THE PRESIDENT
## STEALS THE SHOW

Three years later, on July 4, 1828, President John Quincy Adams was again the honored guest at a canal ceremony—this time to start construction on the Chesapeake and Ohio, which, it was hoped, would run from the outskirts of Washington to the Ohio River.

The C & O was to be a waterway of small consequence compared to the Erie. But at its formal ground-breaking the crowds on hand were treated to a memorable and most unexpected performance put on by the tight-lipped, dignified little Adams. With the preliminary speeches over, the President proceeded to turn the first symbolic spadeful of earth. His spade hit a root. He tried again, but with no better success. "Thus foiled," a newspaper reporter wrote later, "he threw down the spade, hastily stripped off and laid aside his coat, and went

seriously *to work*." The spectators, naturally enough, were delighted. In his *Diary* Adams recalled the incident with glee: "It struck the eye and fancy of the spectators," he wrote, "more than all the flowers of rhetoric in my speech."

But for all the high spirits of the moment, it must, when viewed in the light of subsequent events, take a second place to a far more elaborate inauguration going on in Baltimore at the same time—the grand opening of the B & O Railroad. The C & O Canal never would reach the Ohio; in 1850, competition from the B & O Railroad forced canal construction to halt at Cumberland, Maryland.

## BIG DAY ON
## THE BIG MUDDY

The completion of the Eads Bridge in 1874 was a most momentous occasion. For the United States it was then the greatest bridge in the land, and it spanned the mightiest river in the land with what clearly was to be the building material of the future, steel. For St. Louis, it was not only a source of immense local pride, but a very real and long-needed chance to compete with Chicago, which was presently the main transportation link between East and West.

As on so many previous occasions, July 4 was picked as the appropriate day for celebration. Bunting bedecked the city; a triumphal arch had been put up near the entrance to the bridge and was topped off with a 50-foot-high portrait of James Buchanan Eads, builder of the bridge and very much the hero of the hour. (A motto lettered onto the arch read: "The Mississippi discovered by Marquette, 1673; spanned by Captain Eads, 1874.") Hotels were sold out. People in from out of town were sleeping in the lobbies and baggage rooms, on saloon floors and pool tables. The heat was stupendous.

The big day was marked with a 100-gun salute and a 15-mile parade that wound up crossing the bridge's upper deck while a special train of "palace" cars carried the dignitaries of the day, including President U. S. Grant, across the railroad deck below. Later, at the "Celebration Pavilion" on Washington Avenue,

Captain Eads listened to numerous eulogies of himself and his work, then rose to say, "The love of praise is, I believe, common to all men, and whether it be a frailty or a virtue, I plead no exception from its fascination.

"Yesterday," he continued, "friends expressed to me their pleasure at the thought that my mind was relieved after testing the bridge, but I felt no relief, because I had felt no anxiety." Two days earlier he had conducted his much-publicized public test of the bridge. Fourteen locomotives, with tenders loaded, had crossed over one behind the other, while above them the upper deck was jammed with excited onlookers, who also, apparently, felt no anxiety. Actually, the test was a disappointment to Captain Eads. He had imagined a far grander spectacle in which locomotives would be strung end to end along the lower ramp of the bridge. Unfortunately, fourteen locomotives were all he was able to borrow.

## BUMPER-TO-BUMPER
## BENEATH THE HUDSON

Had a Hollywood press agent handled publicity for the opening of New York's Holland Tunnel on November 12, 1927, he might have advertised that it was: "Seven years in the making. . . . A cast of thousands. . . . Come see and stroll through the world's longest subaqueous tunnel." Then to give the occasion itself a certain 20th-century finesse, he might have draped the tunnel openings with American flags, strung like curtains, that could be drawn electrically at the proper moment from some distant point—from the presidential yacht perhaps, somewhere on the Potomac. Calvin Coolidge would tap the same golden telegraph key that had been used by Woodrow Wilson to open the Panama Canal, and on the far-off shores of the Hudson the flags at both ends of the tunnel would part and the waiting crowds would rush forth.

As it happens, that is just how the occasion was handled, and no press agent could have hoped for a more enthusiastic public response. In the first hour the tunnel was open, some 20,000 people marched the mile and a half from end to end. They laughed, they sang, they acted for all the world, as *The New York Times* reported, "like kids with a new toy." At midnight the tunnel was opened to motorists. With their horns providing a menacing and dissonant prelude to the future, they streamed through by the thousands. Later, one disgruntled driver, having spent over four hours trying to get through, vowed that from then on he would "stick to the ferries." The tunnel's maximum daily capacity had been set at 46,000 vehicles. On its very first day it accommodated more than 51,000.

## HISTORY ON
## THE HOME SCREEN

The completion of the 183-mile-long St. Lawrence Seaway, stretching from St. Lambert near Montreal to Lake Ontario, was hailed by *The New York Times* as "an engineering miracle." It had been a combined venture by the U.S. and Canada and jointly they celebrated its opening on June 26, 1959. At St. Lambert, a haze lingered over the 300-acre ceremonial area adjoining the first lock. Piper bands, trumpeters, a choir, and naval bands from both countries were smartly turned out and the guests of honor included the Queen of England, Elizabeth II, and the President of the United States, Dwight D. Eisenhower. Fireworks went off in a balloon-crowded sky. With the speeches concluded, the official parties boarded the royal yacht *Britannia* for the inaugural voyage upstream.

But for all the traditional hoop-la, it was apparent that times had changed. The spectators, numbering between 10,000 and 15,000, were far fewer than anticipated. For by then, with the mere flick of the knob, anyone who was interested could comfortably view the whole show on television. In fact, within hours after the ceremonies had taken place, Londoners were watching a TV film sent across the Atlantic via telephone cable. And unlike the celebrations of a century before, the newspapers reported no balls or gala parties in celebration of the opening. The seaway was one of the world's greatest engineering feats and it opened up an Atlantic shipping route clear to the western end of Lake Superior; but by then such unheard-of feats of technology had become an expected part of life and the public had grown just a little blasé.

*Sal, the canal mule, has left the towpath to join New Yorkers in one of their more spectacular*

*celebrations: an early 20th-century banquet held in one of the city's new subway tunnels.*

# A HISTORY IN SONG

Gang labor of the kind that built the canals of the last century very often gives rise to a special sort of folk music. Swinging a pick or shovel goes a whole lot easier when there is a good song to swing it to, and keeping time, all together, with ten men digging, or a hundred, makes a 14-hour day go by a bit faster. Like the songs of the foot soldier, those of the canal gangs were generally about the hell of the life they led, the miserable work, the mud, the low pay, and the rest. But underneath all the griping, there was also a sort of hard-nosed humor, and an obvious pride in what they were accomplishing. How the songs got started, who the original composers were, there is no telling. And naturally, with time, tunes changed, new verses were added. The following selections of such surviving songs all relate to the most famous of the canals, the Erie, to the building of it and to the way of life it helped create. There were other work songs, of course, about other canals, and later about the building of the railroads. But interestingly, though perhaps not surprisingly, there would be no music to accompany bridge-building. Bridge work was too precarious a business for much singing on the job. A man had to keep his mind on what it was he was doing, almost every second. It is also no doubt significant that the building of great bridges accompanied the arrival of machines for heavy work. Steam hoists and sawmills, drills, derricks, and steam shovels make a music of their own, and of a sort even the heartiest of singers would not wish to compete with. . . .

One of the songs included here, the final selection, is not about the Erie. It is a tunnel-building saga and among the best known of American folk songs. But it is included because it tells, as does no other song, of the coming of the machine and of the pride in being a man.

## SONG OF THE CANAL

We are digging the Ditch through the mire;
Through the mud and the slime and the mire,
   by heck!
And the mud is our principal hire;
Up our pants, in our shirts, down our neck,
   by heck!
We are digging the Ditch through the gravel,
So the people and freight can travel.

We are digging the Ditch through the gravel,
Through the gravel across the state, by heck!
We are cutting the Ditch through the gravel
So the people and freight can travel,
Can travel across York State, by heck!

· · ·

## PADDY ON THE CANAL

When I landed in sweet Philadelphia,
   The weather was pleasant and clear;
I did not stay long in the city,
   So quickly I shall let you hear,
I did not stay long in the city,
   For it happened to be in the fall,
I never reefed a sail in my rigging,
   'Till I anchored out on the canal.

Chorus:
So fare you well Father and Mother,
   Likewise to old Ireland too;
So fare you well Sister and Brother,
   So kindly I'll bid you adieu.

When I came to this wonderful rampire,
   It filled me with the greatest surprise,
To see such a great undertaking;
   On the like I never opened my eyes
To see full a thousand brave fellows,
   At work among mountains so tall,
To dig through the valleys so level,
   Through rocks, for to cut a canal.

I entered with them for a season,
   My monthly pay for to draw,
And being in very good humor,
   I often sung Erin go Bragh.
Our provision it was very plenty,
   To complain we'd no reason at all,
I had money in every pocket,
   While working upon the canal.

I learned for to be very handy;
   To use both the shovel and spade;
I learned the whole art of canalling:
   I think it an excellent trade.

*I learned for to be very handy,*
*Although I was not very tall,*
*I could handle the "sprig of Shillelah,"*
*With the best man upon the canal.*

*I being an entire stranger,*
*Be sure I had not much to say,*
*The Boss came round in a hurry,*
*Says "boys it is grog time a-day."*
*We all marched up in good order,*
*He was father now, unto us all,*
*Sure, I wished myself from that moment,*
*To be working upon the canal.*

*When at night, we all rest from our labor,*
*Be sure, but our rent is all paid,*
*We laid down our pick, and our shovel,*
*Likewise, our axe, and our spade,*
*We all set a joking together;*
*There was nothing our minds to enthral,*
*If happiness be in this wide world,*
*I am sure it is on the canal.*

To break the monotony of their work, canallers, with the help of strong drink, often whiled away the hours composing tall tales about life on the canal. A sample of their burlesque humor is provided in these verses from "Raging Canal," a lengthy pre-Civil War ballad, in which the canallers portrayed themselves as heroic sailors riding a storm-tossed, perilous sea. Canal is pronounced "can-awl"; and the sea, of course, was really a ditch only 4 feet deep and 40 feet wide. "The E-ri-e" (of which the first verse and refrain follow) is another famous song bemoaning the terrors of shipwreck and the fears of going without drink.

## RAGING CANAL

*Come listen to my story, ye landsmen, one and*
*   all,*
*And I'll sing to you the dangers of that raging*
*   Canal;*
*For I am one of many who expects a watery grave,*
*For I've been at the mercies of the winds and*
*   the waves.*

*I left Albany harbor about the break of day,*
*If rightly I remember 'twas the second day*
*   of May:*
*We trusted to our driver, altho' he was but*
*   small,*
*Yet he knew all the windings of that raging*
*   Canal.*

*It seemed as if the Devil had work in hand*
*   that night,*
*For our oil it was all gone, and our lamps they*
*   gave no light,*
*The clouds began to gather, and the rain began*
*   to fall,*
*And I wished myself off of that raging Canal.*

•  •  •

*But sad was the fate of our poor devoted bark,*
*For the rain kept a pouring faster, and the*
*   night it grew more dark;*
*The horses gave a stumble, and the driver*
*   gave a squall,*
*And they tumbled head and heels into the raging*
*   Canal.*

## THE E-RI-E

*We were forty miles from Albany,*
*Forget it I never shall;*
*What a terrible storm we had that night*
*On the E-ri-e Canal.*

*Refrain:*
*Oh the E-ri-e was a-rising,*
*And the gin was getting low,*
*And I scarcely think we'll get a drink*
*'Till we get to Buffalo,*
*'Till we get to Buffalo.*

Boating on the canal could sometimes be a dangerous enterprise—especially for the steersman of a bull-head boat. The "bull-head" (originally called a "ball-head") refers to a rounded rather than blunt-ended craft that had the cabins built flush against bow and stern; and so the steersman was left with no place to stand but on the cabin roof. With little clearance between roof and on-coming bridges, many a daydreamer who neglected to duck in time was severely crippled or lost his life. The following excerpted verses provide a tongue-in-cheek description of the steersman's fate.

## BOATIN' ON A BULL-HEAD

. . .

They filled me up with beans and shote,
  And lighted me a cob.
They asked me if I could steer a boat
  And offered me a job.

The next mornin' I was boosted
  To the stern-cabin's roof;
With the tiller there I roosted
  And watched the driver hoof.

Now the boat she was a Bull-Head,
  Decked up to the cabin's top;
Many canawlers now are dead
  Who had no place to drop.

(When the bowsman he forgot to yell,
  "Low bridge, duck 'er down!"
The Bull-Head steersman went to hell
  With a bridge-string for a crown.)

. . .

The bridge was only a heave away
  When I saw it 'round the bend
To the Cap a word I didn't say
  While turning end over end.

So canawlers, take my warning:
  Never steer a Bull-Head boat
Or they'll find you some fair mornin'
  In the E-ri-e afloat.

. . .

One popular ballad about the canal era was not a true folk song, but a 1913 tin-pan alley ode. It is a nostalgic farewell to a faithful towpath mule and an almost bygone era.

## LOW BRIDGE! EVERYBODY DOWN
## or FIFTEEN YEARS
## ON THE ERIE CANAL

I've got an old mule and her name is Sal,
Fifteen years on the Erie Canal.
She's a good old worker and a good old pal,
Fifteen years on the Erie Canal.
We've hauled some barges in our day,
Filled with lumber, coal and hay,
And ev'ry inch of the way I know,
From Albany to Buffalo.

Chorus:
Low bridge, ev'rybody down,
Low bridge, we must be getting near a town,
You can always tell your neighbor,
You can always tell your pal,
If he's ever navigated on the Erie Canal.

Steel-driving was the principal job involved in hard-rock tunneling and the steel driver was a very special breed of man. His job was to hammer a long steel drill into solid rock to make holes for the blasting powder. It was work of the roughest kind, demanding super strength, and for which gangs of Negroes were often hired. Among them was 34-year-old John Henry, who swung a 10-pound, steel-driving hammer inside the Big Bend Tunnel on the C & O Railroad near White Sulphur Springs, West Virginia, in 1870. The contractors had decided to try the new steam-powered piston drills, when Henry, the best driver on the Big Bend, fearful that his job was at stake, decided to challenge the new machine.

The contest that followed—with Henry wielding a 20-pound hammer—is now part of our history. There is some doubt as to whether or not Henry actually died from the ordeal, but that he will live on as one of the greatest of American folk heroes, there is no question.

## JOHN HENRY

. . .

*Cap'n says to John Henry,*
*"Gonna bring me a steam drill 'round,*
*Gonna take dat steam drill out on de job,*
*Gonna whop dat steel on down,*
*Lawd, Lawd, gonna whop dat steel on*
*   down."*

*John Henry tol' his cap'n,*
*Lightnin' was in his eye:*
*"Cap'n, bet yo' las' red cent on me,*
*Fo' I'll beat it to de bottom or I'll die,*
*Lawd, Lawd, I'll beat it to de bottom or*
*   I'll die."*

*Sun shine hot an' burnin',*
*Wer'n't no breeze a-tall,*
*Sweat ran down like water down a hill,*
*Dat day John Henry let his hammer fall,*
*Lawd, Lawd, dat day John Henry let his*
*   hammer fall.*

*John Henry went to de tunnel,*
*An' dey put him in de lead to drive;*
*De rock so tall an' John Henry so small,*
*Dat he lied down his hammer an' he cried,*
*Lawd, Lawd, dat he lied down his hammer an'*
*   he cried.*

*John Henry started on de right hand,*
*De steam drill started on de lef' —*
*"Before I'd let dis steam drill beat me*
*   down,*

*I'd hammer my fool self to death,*
*Lawd, Lawd, I'd hammer my fool self to*
*   death."*

. . .

*John Henry tol' his captain,*
*"Looka yonder what I see—*
*Yo' drill's done broke an' yo' hole's done*
*   choke,*
*An' you cain' drive steel like me,*
*Lawd, Lawd, an' you cain' drive steel like*
*   me."*

*De man dat invented de steam drill,*
*Thought he was mighty fine.*
*John Henry drove his fifteen feet,*
*An' de steam drill only made nine,*
*Lawd, Lawd, an' de steam drill only made*
*   nine.*

*De hammer dat John Henry swung*
*It weighed over nine pound;*
*He broke a rib in his lef'-han' side,*
*An' his intrels fell on de groun',*
*Lawd, Lawd, an' his intrels fell on de*
*   groun'.*

*John Henry was hammerin' on de mountain,*
*An' his hammer was strikin' fire,*
*He drove so hard till he broke his pore*
*   heart,*
*An' he lied down his hammer an' he died,*
*Lawd, Lawd, he lied down his hammer an'*
*   he died.*

. . .

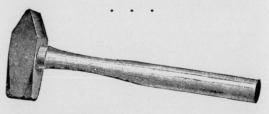

ACKNOWLEDGMENTS

SONG OF THE CANAL—Stanza 1 from *Canal Town* by Samuel Hopkins Adams, Copyright 1944 by Samuel Hopkins Adams; Stanza 2 from *Chingo Smith of the Erie Canal* by Samuel Hopkins Adams, Copyright © 1958 by Samuel Hopkins Adams. Both books published by Random House, Inc. PADDY ON THE CANAL and RAGING CANAL—From *Low Bridge! Folklore and the Erie Canal* by Lionel D. Wyld; Syracuse University Press, 1962. THE E-RI-E—From *The New Song Fest*, ed. by Dick and Beth Best, Copyright 1948, 1955 by R. L. Best; Crown Publishers. BOATIN' ON A BULL-HEAD—From *Body, Boots and Britches* by Harold W. Thompson, Copyright 1939 by Harold W. Thompson, copyright renewed 1967 by Dr. Marian Thompson; J. P. Lippincott Company. LOW BRIDGE—Words and music by Thomas S. Allen, c. 1913 by F. B. Haviland Publishing Company, Inc. JOHN HENRY—Collected, adapted, and arranged by John A. Lomax and Alan Lomax, TRO © Copyright 1934 and renewed 1962, Ludlow Music, Inc., New York, N. Y. Used by permission.

# FURTHER READING

*Asterisk indicates paperback edition.*

## GENERAL

Calhoun, Daniel H. *The American Civil Engineer.* Cambridge, Mass.: The M.I.T. Press, 1960.

Condit, Carl W. *American Building Art.* Vol. I: The Nineteenth Century (1960); Vol. II: The Twentieth Century (1961). New York: Oxford University Press.

Finch, James Kip. *Engineering and Western Civilization.* New York: McGraw-Hill, Inc., 1951.

Finch, James Kip. *The Story of Engineering.* Garden City, N.Y.: Doubleday & Company, Inc., 1960.*

Gramet, Charles. *Highways Across Waterways.* New York: Abelard-Schuman Limited, 1966.

Kirby, Richard S. and Philip G. Laurson. *The Early Years of Modern Civil Engineering.* New Haven: Yale University Press, 1932.

Straub, Hans. *A History of Civil Engineering—An Outline from Ancient to Modern Times.* Cambridge, Mass.: The M.I.T. Press, 1964.

## BRIDGES

Dorsey, Florence L. *Road to the Sea, the Story of James B. Eads and the Mississippi River.* New York: Rinehart & Co., 1947.

Gies, Joseph. *Bridges and Men.* Garden City, N.Y.: Doubleday & Company, Inc., 1963.*

Naruse, Yasuo and Takeshi Kijima (eds.). *Bridges of the World.* Tokyo: Morikita Publishing Co., Ltd., 1964.

Ratigan, William. *Highways over Broad Waters, the Life and Times of David B. Steinman, Bridgebuilder,* Grand Rapids, Mich.: William B. Eerdmans Publishing Co., 1959.

Schuyler, Hamilton. *The Roeblings.* Princeton: Princeton University Press, 1931.

Steinman, David B. *The Builders of the Bridge.* New York: Harcourt, Brace and Company, 1945.

Steinman, David B. and Sara Ruth Watson. *Bridges and Their Builders.* 2nd. rev. ed. New York: Dover Publications, Inc., 1957.*

Talese, Gay. *The Bridge.* New York: Harper & Row, Publishers, 1964.

Trachtenberg, Alan. *Brooklyn Bridge: Fact and Symbol.* New York: Oxford University Press, 1965.

## WATERWAYS

Andrist, Ralph K. *The Erie Canal.* New York: American Heritage Publishing Co., Inc., 1964.

Harlow, Alvin F. *Old Towpaths: The Story of the American Canal Era.* Port Washington, N.Y.: Kennikat Press, Inc., 1926.

Lee, W. Storrs. *The Strength to Move a Mountain.* New York: G. P. Putnam's Sons, 1958.

Mack, Gerstle. *The Land Divided: A History of the Panama Canal and other Isthmian Canal Projects.* New York: Alfred A. Knopf, Inc., 1944.

Payne, Robert. *The Canal Builders.* New York: The Macmillan Company, 1959.

Mabee, Carleton. *The Seaway Story.* New York: The Macmillan Company, 1961.

Waggoner, Madeline Sadler. *The Long Haul West: The Great Canal Era, 1817–1850.* New York: G. P. Putnam's Sons, 1958.

## TUNNELS

Daley, Robert. *The World Beneath the City.* Philadelphia: J. B. Lippincott Company, 1959.

Gies, Joseph. *Adventure Underground.* Garden City, N.Y.: Doubleday & Company, Inc., 1961.

Sandström, Gösta E. *Tunnels.* New York: Holt, Rinehart and Winston, 1963.

Vogel, Robert M. *Tunnel Engineering, A Museum Treatment.* Contributions from The Museum of History and Technology (Bulletin 240, Paper 41). Washington, D.C.: Smithsonian Institution, 1964.*

# INDEX

*Italics indicate illustrations*

# A NOTE ON THIS BOOK

This book was published by the Editors of American Heritage Publishing Company in association with the Smithsonian Institution under the following editorial direction: For the Smithsonian Institution, Anders Richter, Director, Smithsonian Institution Press. For American Heritage, Editor, David G. McCullough; Art Director, Jack Newman; Assistant Art Director, Donald Longabucco; Copy Editor, Susan M. Shapiro; Assistant Editors, Jean Atcheson, Maria Ealand, and Gay Sherry; Picture Editor, Martha F. Grossman; Editorial Assistants, Susan J. Lewis and Karen Olstad.

## ACKNOWLEDGMENTS

The Editors would like to thank the following individuals and organizations for their valuable assistance:

Miss Ruth Brown, North Adams Public Library, North Adams, Mass.

Mr. Stephen Calvert, American Society of Civil Engineers, Library, New York City

Mr. William S. Goodwin, Rensselaer Polytechnic Institute, Library, Troy, N.Y.

Dr. Paul Gugliotta, architect and engineer, New York City

Mr. David Plowden, photographer, New York City

Mr. Richard N. Wright, Secretary-Treasurer of the Canal Society of New York State, Syracuse, N.Y.

## PICTURE CREDITS

Cover, David G. McCullough. 2, American Museum of Photography. 4, Smithsonian Institution. 6–7, *New York Gazette-Post Boy*, June, 1787.
CHAPTER I: 8, David Plowden. 10, 12, Culver Pictures. 13, Erich Hartmann; Magnum. 14–15, Francis & Shaw. 16, Library of Congress. 17, David Plowden. 18, Brown Brothers. 21, David G. McCullough.
CHAPTER II: 22, Library of Congress. 25, Joseph Pickett. *Coryell's Ferry, 1776*. ca. 1914–18. Oil on canvas. 37½ x 48¼". Collection of Whitney Museum of Art, New York. 26–27, Association of American Railroads. 28–29, Francis & Shaw. 30, Cardamone Associates. 32–33, Smithsonian Institution. 35 (left), B. Stuart, *Civil and Military Engineers of America*, 1871. 35 (center and right), Smithsonian Institution.
CHAPTER III: 36, Coverdale and Colpitts. 38, William S. Young, Starrucca Publications. 41, Henry S. Drinker, *Tunneling, Explosive Compounds and Rock Drills*, 1878; North Adams Public Library. 42, Smithsonian Institution. 43, Francis & Shaw. 44–45 (top), Cardamone Associates. 44–45 (bottom),
Smithsonian Institution. 46, George Mowbray, *Trinitroglycerine in Application to the Hoosac Tunnel*, New York Public Library. 48, 49, *Frank Leslie's Illustrated Journal*, December 20, 1873. 50, Culver Pictures. 51, North Adams Public Library.
CHAPTER IV: 52, Robert Phillips. 54–55, George Eastman House. 56–57, *Franklin Institute Journal*, no. 58, 3rd ser. 59, Culver Pictures. 60, David G. McCullough. 62–63, Smithsonian Institution. 64 (top), Culver Pictures. 64 (right), Edward H. Knight, *Knight's American Mechanical Dictionary*, Vol. 1, 1874; Smithsonian Institution. 66–67, Smithsonian Institution. 68–69, Library of Congress. 70–71, David Plowden.
CHAPTER V: 72, *Harper's Magazine*. 74, Culver Pictures. 77, The Old Print Shop. 78, 79, Culver Pictures. 81, Courtesy of the Rensselaer Polytechnic Institute, General Library.
PORTFOLIO: 83, 84 (top), *Harper's New Monthly Magazine*, 1883. 84–85, *Harper's Weekly*, 1870. 85 (top), Cardamone Associates. 85 (bottom), *Frank Leslie's Illustrated Newspaper*, October 15, 1870. 86–87, The Old Print Shop. 87 (top), Cardamone Associates. 88–89, The Old Print Shop. 89 (top), Cardamone Associates. 89 (bottom), *Harper's New Monthly Magazine*, 1883. 90 (top), Cardamone Associates. 90 (bottom), *Harper's Weekly*, 1883. 91, Culver Pictures. 92 (top), Cardamone Associates. 92–93, *Harper's New Monthly Magazine*, 1883. 83–93, engravings hand-tinted by Cal Sacks.
CHAPTER VI: 94, Frances Coleman. 96 (left), Records of the Panama Canal, National Archives. 96 (right), Brown Brothers. 98–99, Douglas Faulkner; Photo Researchers, Inc. 100–101, Smithsonian Institution. 102 (left), 102–103 (top), 103 (top), Julian A. Campbell. 102–103 (bottom), W. B. Bunnell, Manuscript Collections, Carnegie Library, Syracuse University. 104, Culver Pictures. 105, The Port of New York Authority. 106, Ernst Haas; Magnum. 109, Cardamone Associates.
CHAPTER VII: 110, O. Winston Link. 112 (all), Wide World Photos. 114, Barrett Gallagher. 115, Ellis Sawyer; Shostal Associates, Inc. 116–117, O. Winston Link. 118 (left), Steinman, Boynton, Gronquist, and London, Consulting Engineers, New York. 118 (right), Ammann and Whitney, New York. 120–121 (top), Cardamone Associates. 120–121 (bottom), Robert Phillips. 122, G. R. Roberts. 124, Dick Hanley; Photo Researchers, Inc. 126–127, J. R. Eyerman; Black Star.
APPENDIX: 130–131, Smithsonian Institution. 134–135, "Illustrated Description of the Broadway Pneumatic Underground Subway," 1870. 136–141, Bethlehem Steel Corporation. 143, 146–147, 149, Culver Pictures. 150, *Harper's Weekly*, 1884. 151, 158, Culver Pictures.

## ABOUT THE AUTHORS

**DAVID JACOBS,** born in Baltimore, came to New York "to be a painter but found that writing was so much cleaner." He began with a children's book on Renaissance painters, then completed a study of urban renewal in Baltimore, which led to magazine assignments on architectural subjects, and a book, the *Irrelevancy of Architecture*, to be published in 1969. An interest in technology developed naturally from his involvement with city planning, and he is currently at work on a biography of Buckminster Fuller, which is planned for publication in 1970.

**ANTHONY E. NEVILLE,** a professional writer living in Baltimore, has spent most of his life close to the halls of learning: first as a "faculty brat" at Lehigh University, then as a student at Princeton, and later, for several years as editor of the prize-winning *Johns Hopkins Magazine.* "Science and technology always fascinated me," he says, "but no one field predominated. I preferred to snoop around in all of them. I still do." The long association with academic institutions has left its legacy in the scholarly responsibility that he brings to such snooping.